Endors

Your marriage can never be what it was before betrayal.
But it can be better!

COUPLES RECOVERY GUIDE

A 52-WEEK JOURNEY TO
HOPE & HEALING

It only takes one partner to drag the couple into the ditch.
But it takes both partners in order to climb out.

MARK DENISON, D.MIN., MAHS, PSAP
BETH DENISON, CLC, PRC, CPC

FOREWORD

After 30 years of marriage and leading a successful pastoral ministry, our lives and dreams were shattered because of my sexual betrayal. With the help of Mark and Beth Denison and the ministry of *There's Still Hope*, God began to slowly rebuild our lives and restore our marriage.

Today, we experience true intimacy that comes from a place of grace, vulnerability and compassion. If you have experienced the trauma of sexual betrayal and you are uncertain about your next step, we wholeheartedly recommend Mark and Beth Denison's new *Couples Recovery Guide!*

Out of their own journey through sexual betrayal and trauma, God has given the Denisons a special ministry of reconciliation for couples. Regardless of how dark your days appear in this moment, God can still move and work in your marriage! There's Still Hope is more than simply the name of a ministry --- it has become the anthem of the marriage we've always wanted!

James and Lori Franklin
Texas

INTRODUCTION

E very week, millions of sexual addicts fill rooms across the globe, in search of sobriety and recovery. At the same time, far fewer spouses seek their own recovery. And sadly, husbands and wives seek recovery as a couple only in miniscule numbers.

We're here to change that. At least, we'll try.

We did not come to this place lightly. Our journey began with our own individual recovery. For us, that has included multiple clinical disclosures (with polygraphs), extensive therapy, 12-Step work, hundreds of recovery meetings, and exhaustive training that enables us to help others.

Along the way, we have made an exciting discovery. While personal recovery is essential, when we walk this pathway as a couple, well, that changes everything. Couples recovery builds trust and intimacy. It becomes the foundation for a future that illuminates the promise of God — *all things are possible* (Matthew 19:26).

We congratulate you for embarking on this journey with us. Over the next 52 weeks, this is how it will work. Each week, you will complete one chapter, with a laser focus on one essential ingredient to couples recovery. This includes a weekly reading, followed by an exercise. The magic of the process will be the exercises. Each one requires individual work and then work as a couple.

We suggest that you set aside a specific time each week to do the couples' exercises. This won't require much time, but it will require focus.

Couples recovery should be just one part of your overall plan. Below, you will see some of the other resources we offer for women and men seeking a lifetime of freedom.

Welcome to an exciting process. We are honored to walk this pathway with you!

Mark and Beth
There's Still Hope

Other Resources

Coaching, Mentoring, Groups, Blogs

- 12-Week Partner Recovery Group
- 90-Day Recovery Plan
- Freedom Group
- Personal Coaching
- Daily Recovery Minute

Other Books

- 12-Week Partner Recovery Guide
- Porn in the Pew
- Jesus and the 12 Steps
- 365 Days to Sexual Integrity
- Life Recovery Plan
- 90-Day Recovery Guide
- Porn-Free in 40 Days

WEEK ONE
Transparency & Honesty

Honesty is a really big deal with God. Solomon said, "The Lord detests lying lips" (Proverbs 12:22). In the list of "the six things the Lord hates," two of them have to do with honesty: "a lying tongue" and "a false witness" (Proverbs 6:16-19).

Honesty is also a really big deal with marriage. God has the same message for husbands and wives: "Therefore, each of you must put off falsehood and speak truthfully" (Ephesians 4:25).

Comedian Groucho Marx knew a little about honesty in a marriage; he was married for 43 years. Marx quipped, "If you can fake honesty, you've got it made." (This may explain why Marx's 43 years of marriage were spread over three wives.)

The problem is, you can only fake honesty for so long. The Brandon Gaille marketing company offers some sobering data on honesty – or the lack thereof. They found the following:

- Children begin to lie habitually by age three.
- Men lie six times a day.
- Women lie three times a day.
- When meeting someone new, we lie three times in the first ten minutes.
- Spouses lie to each other at least three times a week.

Let's dig deeper, starting with one of the most vivid stories from the Book of Acts.

Ananias and Sapphira
Acts 5:1-11

A husband and wife owned a parcel of land. They did something incredibly generous. Ananias and Sapphira sold their property and gave a portion of the earnings to the church, laying the money at the feet of the church's lead apostle, Peter. This was an admirable act of sacrifice and generosity. There was just one problem.

They lied.

With the full knowledge of his wife, Ananias hatched the plan. He brought the money to Peter, representing it as if their gift was 100 percent of the sale price. Somehow, Peter could tell he was lying. He called Ananias on his dishonesty before God and man. Upon receiving the reprimand of Peter, Ananias dropped dead on the spot.

Three hours later, Sapphira entered the picture, knowing nothing of her husband's tragic death. Peter questioned her about the gift, giving her every chance to come clean. When Sapphira kept up the lie, she met the same fate as her husband. Both husband and wife were buried the same day.

I suggest several lessons to be derived from this story.

- God takes absolute honesty very seriously. William Barclay commented that this story confirms the "stubborn honesty of God."
- When we are honest, we are better for it. I love the story of Oliver Cromwell. When his portrait was finished, he took one look and protested, "Where are my warts?" The artist said, "Sir, I did not paint your warts, in order to make you look better." Cromwell responded, "Do it over. Paint me, warts and all."
- The greater sin is the cover-up. After Ananias completed his plan of setting the money aside, he still had three opportunities to come clean. He had time to reconsider his plan in the time it took to bring the money to Peter; he could have sought more input from Sapphira; and he could have cut Peter off when the apostle called him out for his action.
- Honesty must be a mutual enterprise. (At no point did Sapphira oppose her husband's plan.)
- If we don't value honesty within our marriage, we won't value it anywhere.

It's What Women Want — and Men Need

With most of the couples with whom we work, the wife is the offended partner. Her husband has been unfaithful and has lived a life of addiction that has spiraled out of control. There are many factors that are key to rebuilding the marriage. At the top of that list is absolute honesty and transparency.

Dave Willis addresses this in his groundbreaking book, *The Naked Marriage*. His research produced a list of what he calls "the five things every wife desires and deserves." At the very top of the list is "open, honest, consistent communication."

The addicted spouse has become a world-class liar. This is a part of compartmentalization and covering his steps. He even convinces himself that lying is actually better for his wife. But his secrets eventually come out, and both parties are injured. In her article, "The Complicated Truth About Lying to Your Partner," Dr. Jennice Vilhauer concludes, "While most lies start as self-protection, they end as self-sabotage."

Conclusion

Antonio Stradivari, the great maker of violins, said, "If my hand slacked, I should rob God." What he was saying was that anything less than our best is not good enough. That is especially true with honesty and marriage. To be mostly honest is to be completely dishonest.

One of the things we tell addicts is, "You aren't what you think you are; you are what you hide." To rebuild a marriage shattered by addiction, the wounded spouse must have honesty. Beth tells women, "Trust his behavior, not his words." The good news is that as recovery progresses, honesty can become a solid building block for a wonderful future. Solomon put a romantic spin on it when he said, "An honest answer is like a kiss on the lips" (Proverbs 24:26).

THIS WEEK'S EXERCISE
Let's Get Honest

Honesty is foundational for recovery within the marriage. For sake of simplicity, we will assume the husband is the addict and the wife is the offended spouse. We suggest the following as a strategy to stay open and honest. Check the parts to this plan which you will embrace, then share your list with your spouse, in an effort to arrive at a consensus.

_____ 24-hour rule: The husband will tell his wife of any slip or relapse within 24 hours.

_____ Secrets: The husband shares any interaction or time with someone his wife would want to know about.

_____ Phone: The husband's device will always be available for review.

_____ Covenant Eyes: The husband will get on Covenant Eyes.

_____ Cash: The husband will tell his wife of any cash he has.

_____ Other: _____

FASTT Check-In

This is an excellent system by which the addict communicates his recovery status and struggles with his wife. This can be done every night early on, and may eventually shift to once a week. The husband will share the following with his wife.

Feeling
Activities in recovery
Sobriety update
Threats to sobriety
Tools he is utilizing

WEEK TWO
Boundaries

Setting proper boundaries and putting guardrails in place are a huge part of recovery for both the addicted spouse and the offended partner. Brene Brown said it well: "Daring to set boundaries is about having the courage to love ourselves even when we risk disappointing others." Your boundaries are just that — yours. They need to be specific to your needs. When Paul told believers to "bear one another's burdens" (Galatians 6:2), he was underscoring the need for us to help each other navigate the twists and turns that are common to life — and recovery. Putting boundaries in place does that.

Hezekiah and Sennacherib
2 Chronicles 32

One of our favorite Bible verses for recovery is found in a chapter many of us never read. 2 Chronicles 32:5 tells us that in his effort to protect his people, King Hezekiah built a "second wall of defense."

This is that story.

Assyria was poised to invade Judah, the Southern Kingdom. Assyria's king was a powerful man named Sennacherib. His forces drove all the way to the sacred capital of Jerusalem. Rather than capitulate to the more powerful army, Hezekiah took a stand. The first thing he did was to block off the flow of water in the area, so the Assyrians could not stay long. Then, Hezekiah led a massive building program, first fortifying the existing wall of defense, then building a second, outer wall.

Sennacherib offered a peaceful takeover, if Hezekiah would only surrender. Though massively outmatched, Hezekiah stood firm, calling on God for his protection. After Sennacherib's war of words escalated, "the Lord sent an angel, who annihilated all the fighting men and the commanders and officers in the camp of the Assyrian king. So he withdrew to his own land in disgrace" (32:21).

The story concludes, "So the Lord saved Hezekiah and the people of Jerusalem from the hand of Sennacherib king of Assyria. He took care of them on every side" (32:23).

From this story, I suggest eight lessons.

1. The enemy cannot be defeated in our own power. Hezekiah had defeated other armies, but none were as menacing or powerful as Assyria. The same is true of sex addiction. Overcoming this compulsion is the most daunting task a man can face.

2. We must seek the counsel of others. Before Hezekiah acted, he met with his inner circle of military and spiritual leaders. Likewise, every addict and his spouse must seek the support and counsel of others.

3. We must cut off the addiction at the source. Just as Hezekiah ordered the cutting off of the springs of water, we must cut off every activity that leads to harmful behavior. This means cutting out all porn, getting off social media, and avoiding unnecessary triggers.

4. We must repair what is broken. Before Hezekiah erected a second wall of defense, he rebuilt the first wall. In recovery, we need to give attention to the boundaries that are starting to crumble.

5. We should build another wall of defense. Though Hezekiah never actually needed the second wall, he was wise to put it in place. For the addict, this means enlarging our accountability circle. For the spouse, this means connecting with other wounded spouses, for support and encouragement.

6. Recovery must be offensive, not just defensive. Hezekiah made "weapons and shields" (32:5). While we need a wall of defense, we also must go on the offensive, attacking the problem in a proactive way.

7. We cannot do this without God. Hezekiah worked as though Jerusalem's defense depended on him, then he prayed as though it depended on God.

8. God must get the glory. Immediately after the victory, King Hezekiah paused to lead his people in a time of worship and sacrifice to God.

Tips for Building Guardrails

Boundaries must serve both spouses. To fail to put up a "second wall of defense" is to invite danger. As Henry Cloud says, "You get what you tolerate." Speaking for wives, Brene Brown writes, "When we fail to set boundaries and hold people accountable, we feel used and mistreated." While each partner needs his or her personal boundaries, we suggest the following guidelines when putting these guardrails in place.

1. Start with non-sexual guardrails.

Nick Stumbo, executive director of Pure Desire, writes, "The best guardrails I have don't address my past addiction at all. They address all the patterns that were part of my behaviors." For me (Mark) this means spending quality time with Beth, not staying up late at night watching television, eating right, getting daily exercise, staying off social media, connecting with a group of men, being active in my church, reading Scripture and praying daily, and indulging in a few healthy habits. For me (Beth), it means, on a daily basis, making my spiritual, physical, mental, and emotional needs a priority, and saying "no" to things that jeopardize these, even at the risk of the other person's displeasure.

2. Put your guardrails in concrete.

I (Mark) remember my first car ride in the mountains. Our family was on a vacation in California when I was 13 years old. As we drove up this winding road, a slight error by the driver (my dad) would have sent us over the cliff. Dad assured us that we were okay, as there were guardrails in place. Of course, it would have been possible to still drive over the edge, even with the guardrails in place, but it was of comfort to see these rails were set in stone. They were permanent and strong. The same must be true for our guardrails. Both the addicted spouse and his partner need to prayerfully identify specific guardrails that will not be compromised.

3. Guardrails are positive.

Don't think of these guardrails as a negative thing. Stumbo says, "Our guardrails should increase our sense of joy, health, and well-being. They not only protect us from bad places, they also redirect us toward good places." Examples might include plenty of sleep, weekly date nights, weekly worship, and consistent recovery meetings.

Conclusion

Author Doreen Virtue wrote, "Boundaries are a part of self-care. They are healthy, normal, and necessary." This is true for both spouses. Every couple — especially those affected by sexual addictions — needs to take seriously the issue of boundaries. Guardrails must be erected carefully, with consideration for the emotional needs of both partners. It is wise to revisit these boundaries from time to time. Nothing will do more to keep the recovery and marriage on track.

THIS WEEK'S EXERCISE
Setting Up Boundaries

It will be interesting to see how your boundaries list differs from your spouse's. The purpose here is to put up boundaries that will bring a level of comfort and begin to rebuild trust for the offended spouse, usually the wife. The exercise is simple. If you are the wounded spouse, make a list of boundaries you want your partner to put in place. If you are the sex addict, write a list of boundaries you will choose to put in place. Then compare lists. Where there are differences, tie goes to the offended spouse. She is the one who needs to feel comfortable.

- _____
- _____
- _____
- _____
- _____
- _____
- _____
- _____
- _____
- _____

WEEK THREE
Gratitude

Maintaining an attitude of gratitude in the midst of discovery and early recovery is a high order, to be sure. Even on the one day of the year dedicated to thanksgiving, gratitude becomes an after-thought for most of us. Humorist Erma Bombeck observed, "Thanksgiving dinner takes 18 hours to prepare and 12 minutes to consume --- the length of halftime." Charlie Brown noted, "I can't cook a Thanksgiving dinner. All I can make is cold cereal and maybe toast."

For too many of us, addiction has turned our Thanksgiving dinner into cold cereal. It's not that we don't want to offer thanks, it's just that we put it on hold. "After Jim gets sober, I'll offer thanks." "When Cindy quits surfing dating sites, I'll have a heart filled with gratitude." "I'll be so thankful once I have my marriage back."

The Bible is full of stories of thanksgiving. Let's consider just three.

Story #1 --- Hannah
1 Samuel 1:1-28

The story of Hannah and Samuel is made for Hollywood. There was a man named Elkanah who had two wives, Peninnah and Hannah. While Peninnah had children, Hannah remained barren. Any woman who knows the heartache of an empty womb can feel Hannah's pain. In biblical times, the pressure of having children was much greater than it is today. God stepped in and used barrenness to reveal his purpose several times throughout Scripture.

Elkanah and his family went to Shiloh to offer sacrifices to the Lord. Hannah was overwhelmed with sadness because she had no children. Eli, the high priest, found her weeping from a broken heart before God.

At first, Eli assumed from her behavior that Hannah must have been drunk. Hannah quickly explained her grief and petition before the Lord. She committed to dedicate her child to God if he would grant her prayer. Eli responded,

"Go in peace, and the God of Israel will grant your petition which you have asked of him" (1:17).

When Hannah left the priest, she was "no longer sad" (1:18). Note that she did not wait for her prayer to be answered before she acted as if her prayer had been answered. Hannah named her son Samuel, "because I have asked for him from the Lord" (1:20). The Hebrew name Samuel meant "asked of the Lord."

When Samuel was old enough, Hannah brought him back to serve the high priest and reminded Eli of that night when he had found her weeping. She then broke out with a song of thanksgiving, recorded in 1 Samuel 2:1-10.

Lesson: We are to thank God for his promises, not just his blessings.

Story #2 --- Mary
Luke 1:26-56

Mary surely understood the weight of her circumstances as a pregnant virgin. And yet, as she realized that she was pregnant with the son of God, she rejoiced in the blessings of being God's chosen vessel. Her choice to view her circumstances as a blessing when the world around her would have shouted the exact opposite stands as a testament to all who read her story.

Mary went to see her cousin, and it was there that she shared what became known as The Magnificat (Latin, "My soul magnifies the Lord"). This would be included among the first eight ancient Christian hymns, and it continues to be sung regularly in Catholic and Lutheran churches.

Consider a few outtakes from Mary's message to her cousin Elizabeth.

- "My soul glorifies the Lord" (1:46).
- "My spirit rejoices in God my Savior" (1:47).
- "The Mighty One has done great things for me" (1:49).
- "Holy is his name" (1:49).
- "He has performed mighty deeds" (1:51).

Lesson: Some of God's greatest blessings are not understood at first.

Story #3 --- The Leper
Luke 17:11-19

One day Jesus encountered ten lepers. Because of their disease they were not allowed to approach Jesus, but this did not keep them from reaching out to him. They shouted to him, "Jesus, Master, have mercy on us!" (11:13).

Jesus told them to go show themselves to the priests, as they were the ones with the power to officially declare the lepers healed, allowing them to return to society. As they went away, the Bible says, "they were cleansed" (11:14).

Then the story gets really interesting. Without pause, one of the ten returned to thank Jesus. This man was a Samaritan, thereby being a man without rank in the eyes of the Jews.

Let's pick up the story there.

"So Jesus answered and said, 'Were there not ten cleansed? But where are the nine? Were there not any found who returned to give glory to God except this foreigner?' And he said to him, 'Arise, go your way. Your faith has made you well'" (17:17-19).

All ten lepers were healed, but only one returned to offer thanks. All ten received a blessing, but only one became a blessing. While the other nine experienced God's healing, only one recognized his goodness. And while all ten men were healed, only the thankful Samaritan was declared "well."

Lesson: Only the thankful become truly whole.

Principles on Gratitude

1. Make a gratitude list.

Paul wrote, "Let the peace of Christ rule in your hearts, since as members of one body you were called to peace. And be thankful" (Colossians 3:15). For Paul, gratitude was not optional; it was a command. A simple way to obey this command is to make a gratitude list. The words first published by Johnson Oatman, Jr., in 1897 still ring true today: "Count your blessings, name them one by one; and it will surprise you what the Lord has done."

2. Thanksgiving doesn't follow blessing; blessing follows thanksgiving.

We are told, "Give thanks to the Lord, for he is good; his love endures forever" (1 Chronicles 16:34). This verse comes with no conditions. Do what Hannah and Mary did. Offer thanks before the blessing. The psalmist understood this principle when he beckoned, "Enter his house with thanksgiving" (Psalm 100:4). Note the word "enter." We are to pour out thanks to God as we enter his presence, not waiting until the first note is played for the first song.

3. There is a huge difference between "for" and "in."

The Bible says to "give thanks in all circumstances" (1 Thessalonians 5:18). We are to offer thanks in our addiction, in our recovery, in the discovery, in the disclosure. It would be crazy to thank God for your addiction or for the events that undercut your world. But we can remain thankful in the midst of the storm.

for not disclosing is for the addict to protect himself, there is legitimacy to this point. But we must understand that not knowing everything will keep our wives in an unsafe place. The damage caused by disclosure is far less than the damage caused by them not knowing. A further point — most spouses suspect we have actually done more than we really have.

2. We recommend using a C.S.A.T.

A certified sex addiction therapist holds the most strenuous training and clinical experience in the field. We urge clients to reach out to Dr. Milton Magness, founder of Hope & Freedom, when considering a disclosure. He has personally trained some of the best C.S.A.T. counselors in America. For more information, go to hopeandfreedom.com.

3. We strongly support polygraphs.

Let's put one myth to bed — they really are accurate. We tell couples, "One thing is for sure. A correctly administered polygraph is far more trustworthy than the untested word of an addict." We understand the resistance to taking a polygraph. We hear it all the time. "Marriages need to be built on trust." "What if I'm telling the truth, but the polygraph says I lied?" "Unless I'm going to take them for the rest of my life, why should I take one now?"

Let us offer a few observations at this point.

a. If you have a false failure (extremely unlikely), you can retake the polygraph, using a different polygrapher if you choose.
b, The addicted spouse should actually want to take polygraphs, out of his commitment to restore trust in the marriage.
c. Polygraphs are not forever. It's true that it is not healthy for the marriage to require polygraphs for years to come. But for the initial disclosure and follow-ups for the next year or two, most spouses find these very helpful. (I have committed to taking a polygraph anytime Beth wants/needs me to for the rest of our lives.)
d. The addicted spouse is imminently more likely to tell all under the threat of a polygraph. This may be the best argument. We have never met an addict who, upon hearing he will not have to take a polygraph, became more forthcoming with his disclosure. If the wife needs a disclosure with a polygraph in order to rebuild trust and feel safe, her husband should want to give her this gift.

A Final Word

Will Rogers said, "Live in a way that you'd be happy to sell your pet parrot to the town gossip." Apart from a pet parrot, a clinical disclosure is the best way to begin the process of rebuilding trust. Here's what we know about sex addicts. They long to be fully known and truly loved. In their addiction, they picked one or the other. The thinking is, "If she really knew me, she wouldn't love me, and if she really loves me, it's because she doesn't really know me." That's a horrible way to live. The addict will never know true freedom until he tells all to the one he loves, and allows the healing to begin.

THIS WEEK'S EXERCISE
Decide on a Disclosure

The process of a full clinical disclosure is important. You are unwise to jump out and do a disclosure on your own, without professional guidance. If you are the addict, your disclosure will include all past sexual activities outside of marriage. You will write this out in great detail. If you are the wife, after you receive this disclosure, read in the presence of a therapist, you will then be directed to write a response letter. Then, the addict will generally be instructed to write a response letter to that.

This exercise is different for each spouse.

For the Husband (Addict)

You must simply decide whether you are willing to do a full, clinical disclosure for your wife. And you must decide if you are willing to take a polygraph, as well.

Are you willing to do a full, clinical disclosure? _____

Are you willing to take a polygraph? _____

For the Wife (Non-addict)

We estimate that about 90 percent of women want a full disclosure; they demand complete honesty. You have to decide if that is you.

Do you want to receive a full clinical disclosure from your husband? _____

Do you want him to take a polygraph? _____

For Both of You

Now, you should discuss your individual work. Discuss your willingness and expectations in terms of a disclosure. Try to come to an agreement on moving forward.

WEEK FIVE
Self-Care

L ucille Ball said, "Love yourself first, and everything else falls in line. You really have to love yourself to get anything done in this world." Unfortunately, self-care is rarely a priority, either for the addict or his spouse. The addict sees himself as unworthy, while his wife is often consumed with maintaining a semblance of normality in her quest to keep her head above water. But self-care is a reliable component of recovery for the individual and for the marriage.

Jesus said, "Are you tired? Worn out? Burned out on religion? Come to me. Get away with me and you'll recover your life. I'll show you how to take a real rest. Walk with me and work with me; watch how I do it. Learn the unforced rhythms of grace. I won't lay anything heavy or ill-fitting on you. Keep company with me and you'll learn to live freely and lightly" (Matthew 11:26-30 MSG). And Jesus practiced what he preached. "As often as possible Jesus withdrew to out-of-the-way places for prayer" (Luke 5:16 MSG).

The Second Command of Jesus is that we love others "as we love ourselves" (Matthew 22:39). Note, we must love ourselves first. That's what this week's work is about. Let's get started with the story of the most fascinating preacher of the Old Testament.

The Story of Elijah
I Kings 19:1-18

Raise a child to life. Check. Stare down 450 prophets of Baal. Check. Bring down fire from heaven. Check. Eat food provided by ravens. Check. Eat food brought by an angel. Check. Multiply the oil. Check. Pray water down from heaven. Check.

Stand up to one woman's verbal threats. Run!

The man who facilitated 16 recorded miracles over eight years could stare down 850 false prophets at one time. But when one woman issued a threat, he ran away --- as far and as fast as he could.

We pick up the story in I Kings 19.

"Elijah was afraid and ran for his life" (19:3). First, he traveled 80 miles south, to the city of Beersheba. Then he walked a day's journey into the wilderness. It seemed to be the perfect place to hide. Then, after finally taking a seat, Elijah "prayed that he might die" (19:4). He said, "I have had enough; take my life" (19:4). With that, he collapsed into a deep sleep.

Elijah was awakened by an angel. The first thing the angel said was not, "Repent you idiot!" No, the angel said, "Get up and eat" (19:5). He was provided baked bread and water.

His journey then took him to Horeb, "the mountain of God" (19:8). The trip took 40 days. Elijah discovered a cave, which provided shade, cool nights, and rest. And finally, after six weeks on the run, Elijah was ready to meet with God. He expressed his grievances. God didn't argue with him or deny his pain. What he did was to provide an intimate spiritual encounter. After witnessing a powerful wind, an earthquake, and fire, Elijah heard God speak in a quiet whisper. Only then did God say, "Go back the way you came" (19:15).

Lessons from Elijah

Several lessons jump from this story. Elijah stood on the brink of suicide. He was too tired to kill himself, so he asked God to do the favor. Instead, God picked the preacher up, dusted him off, and eventually sent him back home. What can we learn about self-care from this story?

1. We fail by relying on our strengths.

Charles Spurgeon was captivated with this story, and he preached from it often. Spurgeon observed, "Elijah failed in the very point at which he was strongest, and that is where most men fail. In Scripture, it is the wisest man who proves himself to be the greatest fool; just as the meekest man, Moses, spoke hasty and bitter words. Abraham failed in his faith, and Job in his patience; so, he who was the most courageous of all men, fled from an angry woman."

2. Depression drives us into isolation.

It wasn't enough that he had already run 80 miles from home. Beyond the distant city of Beersheba, Elijah secluded himself even more. This is common for spouses of sex addicts. In their pain, they withdraw into the pain of isolation.

3. Suicide is a curse that cannot be ignored.

Our family has been rocked by suicide. We know, firsthand, that pain is real and too often missed by others. One day, Elijah stood as the most powerful voice for God anywhere in the world. The next chapter finds him crying for God to take his life. (Interestingly, the man who prayed for death never died.)

4. There is a limit to our pain.

Elijah spoke three very revealing words: "It is enough" (19:4). His work was stressful and exhausting. Worse yet, Elijah did not see the results he had hoped for. The revival on Mounty Carmel was short lived. Worse yet, it seems that Elijah took all of this on himself. "I am no better than my fathers" (19:4). He thought he had somehow failed. That is how addicts feel and that is how spouses feel.

5. Self-care is spiritual.

The angel sent from God instructed Elijah to care for his physical needs, which would include food, water, and rest. In your pain and hopelessness, there is nothing you will ever do that is more spiritual than taking care of yourself.

6. Self-care is the foundation for encountering God.

It was after — not before — Elijah practiced self-care that he heard the quiet whisper of God. It was after he ate, drank, and found rest that he was prepared to encounter God on the mountain. Sometimes, the next best thing we can do is not to go to church, read the Bible, or even pray. Our first order of business may be to take a nap.

Practical Ways to Practice Self-Care

The list of ways to practice self-care is limitless. The benefits of self-care cannot be overstated. Just as Jesus needed self-care, as did Elijah before him, you need to learn to practice self-care. Your marriage and recovery depend on it. Here are just a few practical suggestions.

1. Get plenty of sleep.

Sleep can have a huge effect on how you feel, both emotionally and physically. Dr. Tchiki Davis warns, "Not getting enough sleep can even cause major health issues."

2. Eat right.

When things aren't right with your self-care, you can feel it in your gut — literally. Eat a healthier diet. This will make you feel better, and when you feel better, recovery becomes easier.

3. Do a Recovery Day.

We recommend that recovering sex addicts strive to set aside one day per month to focus on their recovery. This day should include a 12-Step meeting, casual activity outdoors, prayer, journaling, and reading recovery materials.

4. Get some exercise.

Keep moving. Exercise can boost your mood and reduce stress. It will also help you to become more fit, which builds confidence and self-esteem.

5. Learn to say no.

Annie Lamott coined the phrase, "No is a complete sentence." Warren Buffett says, "Successful people say no to almost everything." Self-care is about learning to say no.

6. Take a short trip.

The benefit of getting away by yourself for just a few days is amazing. It provides relaxation and a re-set that we all need. Use this time to do something just for yourself.

7. Schedule self-care time.

Your to-do list includes appointments with everyone but yourself. Until you take self-care seriously enough to schedule time for these activities, it probably won't happen.

Conclusion

Self-care is as spiritual and necessary as prayer, Bible reading, and going to church. We love the words of Diane von Furstenberg: "It is so important to take time for yourself and find clarity. The most important relationship is the one you have with yourself." Elijah was a man of profound strength. In his hour of fear and pain, he practiced self-care. We cannot afford to do less.

THIS WEEK'S EXERCISE
Be Kind to Yourself

Our favorite physician, Dr. Seuss, said, "Be who you are and say how you feel, because those who mind don't matter, and those who matter don't mind."

The fact is, you matter. A lot. You matter to God and you *should* matter to you!

The next time you fly on a commercial aircraft, listen as the flight attendant gives instructions prior to take-off. In addition to telling you pertinent pieces of information such as how to turn your seat into a flotation device (even if you are flying over Nebraska), he or she will give a quick lesson on oxygen. They will tell you that if the plane falls out of the sky, oxygen masks will drop down. And your first job is to get your own oxygen mask in place. Only then are you able to help those around you.

You can't help anyone else more than you help yourself. This week, we offer a four-step exercise.

Step 1 — A balanced approach

Name one thing you can do in each area for self-care:
- Physical:

  _____

- Spiritual:

  _____

- Emotional:

  _____

- Mental:

  _____

Step 2 — A timely approach

Name one thing you will do for self-care:
- Each day:

  _____

- Each week:

  _____

- Each month:

  _____

- Each year:

  _____

Step 3 — A couples approach

Share your list with your husband or wife.

Step 4 — A selfless approach

Write down two things you will do to help your spouse meet his or her needs for self-care:
- _____

- _____

WEEK SIX
Rebuilding Trust

F riedrich Nietzsche's words represent the heart of every betrayed spouse: "I'm not upset that you lied to me. I'm upset that from now on I can't believe you." As painful as the deception is, the fact is that this initial breach of trust is more the seed than the harvest. By that we mean that deception is never isolated; it is symptomatic of a problem on a much grander scale.

As Albert Einstein said, "Whoever is careless with the truth in small matters cannot be trusted with important ones." For most wounded spouses, the doubts began years before the full discovery was made. Your husband was late coming home from work. He kept his phone out of sight most of the time. There were text messages he didn't want you to see. The $20 in his wallet went missing without explanation.

Nothing big. It always starts small. You want to believe him. After all, your husband is a good provider, teaches a class at church, and is a great dad. Surely, any hints of impropriety are not well-founded.

And then you discover something for which there is no good explanation. The trust has been shattered. A downward spiral of uneven emotions and frantic bouts of depression ensue. You are faced with two binary choices: (a) leave him, or (b) ignore what you see.

Actually, there is a third — and much better — choice. Mira Kirshenbaum says it like this: "What's burned is burned, but what's broken can heal. And broken trust in a relationship is not like a house on fire." In other words, there is hope.

Rebuilding trust requires work by both parties — the offender and the offended. The wounded spouse often balks at this notion. "He messed up, so why should I have to do the work?" she reasons. No, it's not fair that the wounded spouse should have to do anything to rebuild the relationship. But that is reality.

Doe Zantamata writes on this subject. "Rebuilding trust when it's been broken is not dependent only on the person who has broken it, or how many times they can prove they are honest. It depends on the person who has decided not to trust anymore. Though they may be totally justified in their decision to not trust, as long as they choose not to, the relationship has no hope of survival. If or when they decide to trust again, there is hope reborn."

That's what we're going to talk about this week — how to rebuild trust.

Three Men with Bags of Gold
Matthew 25:14-30

Shortly before his death, Jesus told his disciples a poignant story about a wealthy man who placed his trust in three servants. It may be the best story on trust in the Bible. While the Scripture describes the man's wealth in monetary terms that were familiar to the audience of that day, I will take the liberty to use the modern example of U.S. dollars.

Here's what happened.

A wealthy man was going away for a while. He entrusted $1 million in the hands of three servants, or friends. To one he gave $600,000. To his second friend he gave $300,000, and to the third he gave $100,000. The wealthy man expected the men to not only protect his money, but to grow it.

While the man was away, the first guy invested the money wisely, and doubled the funds. The second friend did the same. They now had $1.2 million and $600,000, respectively. But the third servant was filled with fear, so he buried his portion, rather than try to grow it.

When the traveler returned, he listened to each man's financial report. To the first two friends, he rewarded them with more responsibility, as they had proven themselves trustworthy. His message to the third man, who had failed to live up to his expectations, was quite different. He took his $100,000 and gave it to the first servant to manage.

We see several lessons from this story.

1. Relationship breeds trust.

Clearly, the wealthy man had a level of trust in each servant by virtue of their working relationship. A man of that wealth could have entrusted his money to any number of servants, but he chose these three. There was a relationship in place that gave him confidence.

In marriage, we have "change in our pockets" starting out. Every time we do something to build trust, more change goes in the pocket. When we break that trust, change comes out. With the discovery of infidelity, our pockets are emptied. Rebuilding trust, or putting change back in our pockets, is a long process.

2. Trust can be grown.

The traveler only gave his first two servants more responsibility after they proved themselves with their first opportunity. Likewise, in marriage, we can build trust over years, but only by what we do. Notice, the wealthy man didn't bother to ask his servants how they would do with his money. He only cared about actions.

I (Beth) always tell my clients who have been betrayed by their husband, "Trust their behaviors, not their words." Trust can be grown and regrown, but only by what we do.

3. What we do when we are "caught" matters as much as what we did wrong.

The servant who buried his money was confronted by the rich man. He had two options. He could own what he had done, confess it, and commit to a better future. Or he could blame and deflect. He chose the latter. He blamed the rich man for being "harsh," and he blamed his own fear of failure. We will never know how the rich man might have responded had he owned his failure, but by not owning it, he brought the harshest of judgments upon himself.

4. The reward for work well done is more work to do.

This is especially true of recovery. When we climb one mountain, complete one step, reach one sobriety date — there is more to do still. We never arrive at the rainbow's edge. In the parable before us, the traveler didn't say to the first two men, "Well done, take a break." Rather, he said, "Well done, go do some more." It is by working our recovery that we keep our recovery.

5. Those who fail are those who do not try.

When I (Mark) work with a client who does recovery work, but still relapses, I'm okay with that. I work with him to improve his plan and build more disciplines into his life. Eventually, he'll get there. I'm far less tolerant with the man who barely works his recovery, then seems shocked when he falls. I have determined to follow the counsel of my mentor, Dr. Milton Magness, who says, "Never work their recovery harder than they do." The third servant in our parable was found guilty, not for lack of success, but for lack of effort.

Six Principles in Rebuilding Trust

If your marriage has been rocked by addiction and lying, we can guarantee two things: (a) pain, and (b) hope. The betrayal will bring more horrific pain than the wounded spouse will ever know otherwise. But with the right efforts and God's healing, hope is always available. We suggest you take the following steps in order to rebuild trust.

1. The addict must own his betrayal.

Unlike the third servant in the parable, the addict cannot blame anyone but himself for the pain he has inflicted on his spouse. You may be thinking, "But I didn't ask for the trauma, abuse, and isolation that drove me into addiction." That's very true. You are not to be blamed for incurring your addiction, but for living in it and not getting out of the ditch sooner. And never forget — every time the addict lies or acts out, he has chosen to do something in the moment that he did not have to do. So own it.

2. The addict must get help for himself.

Before the addict can help his wife, he must help himself. That means getting into recovery, attending 12-Step meetings, working the Steps, and seeing a therapist. And we want to be clear here. The addict must get help for himself — not for his wife. His own sanity and worth as a person are the keys here, not saving his marriage.

3. The addict must do a disclosure.

The wounded spouse needs to know what she's dealing with. That requires 100 percent knowledge of everything. She cannot heal from something she does not know. This means committing to a three-day intensive and disclosure, preferably with a CSAT (Certified Sex Addiction Therapist). A polygraph is recommended.

4. The couple should start a weekly recovery night.

Our ministry offers multiple useful tools at this point. A weekly evening, in which the couple commits to one hour of recovery exercises is vital to rebuilding trust — one small step at a time. Recovery nights are well-suited for honesty and transparency.

5. Create a plan.

Trust isn't rebuilt quickly, nor is it rebuilt easily. A detailed plan is called for. As a couple, you should sit down and create a daily plan for both the husband and wife, to foster trust. This plan should include recovery nights and recovery work by both spouses.

6. Trust his actions, not his words.

Let us repeat: "Trust his behaviors, not his words." In order to find healing and to rebuild trust, the wounded spouse must become observant, noticing the good work the addict is doing in his own recovery. But never forget, addicts are liars. It is imperative to trust the addict's behaviors, not his words.

Conclusion

Frank Crane said, "You may be deceived if you trust too much, but you will live in torment if you don't trust enough." The wounded spouse will not heal in the relationship apart from rebuilding trust. Is it fair that she should have to do her own recovery work? Absolutely not. Is it fair that she should put herself out there where she can be hurt again? Not at all. But if the marriage is to make it, trust must be rebuilt. And for both spouses, this requires risk, but without that risk they will never reap the rewards. Anurag Prakash Ray said, "To forgive someone who hurt you is easy, but to trust them again is next to impossible." While this is true, the good news is that "next to impossible" and "impossible" are not the same thing.

THIS WEEK'S EXERCISE
Steps to Trust

Many call it "D-Day." It is the day of discovery. The addiction or affair becomes known. It might have been a number on a phone. Maybe a text message. Or a hidden gift. Perhaps unexplained cash. Something didn't add up, and the truth came out.

If you have committed to recovery as a couple, the long process of rebuilding trust must be embraced head-on. And if you are the offender, remember, your wife needs total honesty. Partial honesty isn't good enough.

We like to use the analogy of change in the pocket. Every time you lie to your wife, a little change comes out. When you do the good work of recovery, change goes in. If you do enough things that breach the trust, your change will eventually run out. You become relationally bankrupt.

So this exercise is all about putting change in the pocket.

Part A — Ladies, what do you want?

List the things you want your husband to do to rebuild trust.

_____

_____

_____

_____

_____

_____

Part B — Men, what will you do?

_____

_____

_____

_____

_____

_____

_____

Part C — Talk it out.

Now come together as a couple and discuss a way forward. Agree on the things you will do as a couple to rebuild trust.

WEEK EIGHT
Accountability

Accountability is a personal thing for me (Mark). When I was 15 years of age and a new believer, I was introduced to a young man, five years my senior. I entered into an accountability relationship with this college student. Jimmy became the most important man in my life, apart from my father and pastor. He spent untold hours with me in God's Word, prayer, and demonstrating the Christian life for me.

The missing link for recovery — and life — is often accountability. In *Goal Setting to Live Your Dreams*, Bola Anada Sokunbi writes, "Most goals people set are not achieved because they are not held accountable for them." Both the addict and his spouse must develop personal accountability if they are to get through the rough patches and triggering periods that are an inevitable part of recovery.

Let's dive into the story of one man whose undeniable greatness was predicated on the levels of accountability he built into his early life as a follower of Christ.

Paul's Amazing Story of Accountability
Acts 9:10-30
Galatians 1:18-20

Before Paul was an apostle, the author of one-third of the New Testament, and the most significant figure in the early church, he made himself accountable to a series of mature believers. Paul's story is so powerful that it cannot be contained in a single book. (We will be in both Acts and Galatians.)

Paul experienced the original Damascus Road conversion. The radical life-change of this historic Jewish leader and persecutor of Christians consummated with his blindness outside the city of Damascus. This left him dependent on others, perhaps for the first time in his adult life. And that is when he became accountable to a series of more mature believers, before launching his public ministry.

1. Ananias

Paul's first accountability partner was a man named Ananias. The Bible says simply, "In Damascus there was a disciple named Ananias" (Acts 9:10). God directed this servant to a home in Damascus where Paul had been led after his blindness. For three days, Paul had fasted and prayed in this home. A reluctant Ananias agreed to visit Paul, pray for him, and he may have been the man who baptized him (9:11-19).

2. The disciples of Damascus

"Saul spent several days with the disciples in Damascus" (Acts 9:19). It is important to note that these were not the original 12 disciples of Christ. That relationship would come a bit later. We know very little about these disciples in Damascus, but they clearly encouraged Paul and helped him to develop his faith in Jesus. The result of their ministry to him laid the groundwork for Paul to "preach in the synagogues that Jesus was the Son of God" (9:20). It is important to note that Paul was in no hurry to move into a place of leadership, until he had been further developed in his early ministry and was accountable to those around him. It was three years before he went to Jerusalem (Galatians 1:18).

3. Barnabas

Persecution would eventually drive Paul from Damascus. His associates helped him escape his pursuers, and he traveled to Jerusalem. While the Scripture merely says "he came to Jerusalem" (9:26), this journey covered 135 miles, a significant distance in that day. Clearly, Paul was on a mission, setting his eyes on the holy city. But he didn't stand a chance of being accepted by the leaders of the early church until he found cover from someone as respected as Barnabas. So Paul submitted to the leadership of his new friend, which opened doors for ministry he could not have enjoyed otherwise.

4. Peter

While Luke's account in Acts tells us that Paul became accountable to the original disciples of Jesus, Paul later gave us more details. In his letter to the churches of Galatia, he wrote the following: "After three years I went up to Jerusalem to visit Cephas [Peter] and remained with him fifteen days. But I saw none of the other apostles except James the Lord's brother" (Galatians 1:18-20). Peter was the clear leader among the early disciples, followed by James. Paul made himself accountable to both.

5. The 12 disciples

Once he was fully introduced to the apostles, Paul "stayed with them and moved about freely in Jerusalem" (Acts 9:28). His circle of accountability was now complete. Before setting out on his three missionary journeys and becoming the great church planter of the New Testament, Paul entered freely into accountability relationships with those who had come before him.

A Specific Accountability Plan

The primary reason accountability does not work is that it is not tried. You have to go all in. Successful accountability is not meeting with a few friends over coffee to talk about your spouse. It is useless unless you engage the process on several very intentional levels. Following are the basic components of successful accountability.

1. Be accountable to God.

Solomon said, "Here is my final conclusion: Fear God and obey his commands" (Ecclesiastes 12:13). Paul adds, "Each of us will give a personal account to God" (Romans 14:12). When we think about accountability, we usually think about a relationship with another person or some action we can take to give confidence to our spouse. But accountability is vertical before it can be horizontal. Both the addict and the spouse must see themselves as accountable to God before they are accountable to anyone else.

2. Write an accountability statement.

This doesn't need to be long, but it needs to include the rationale behind your desire for accountability and what steps you are willing to take to maintain personal accountability. Write it down, and keep it handy. You may need to refer to it often. Brian Dive writes, "Accountability is a statement of personal promise, not to yourself and to the people around you, to deliver specific defined results" (*The Accountable Leader*).

3. Know your triggers and have a plan.

Your triggers will be unique to you. Know what tends to set you off — toward relapse, anger, or isolation. Have a plan in place for how you will respond when these triggers hit full force. Be proactive with your plan. Hal Elrod said, "The moment you take responsibility for everything in your life is the moment you can change everything in your life."

4. Join a group.

Accountability needs several layers. Before becoming accountable to an individual, we recommend becoming accountable to a group. The natural outlet for this is a recovery group. There are many options here. Of course, we recommend our Freedom Groups (for male sex addicts) and Partner Recovery Groups (for women).

5. Get an accountability partner.

"Two people are better off than one, for they can help each other succeed" (Ecclesiastes 4:9). Don't rush into this. Your accountability partner needs to meet the following criteria: (a) strong spiritual walk, (b) greater progress in their recovery than you have, (c) absolute confidentiality, (d) man or woman of prayer, (e) willing to ask you the hard questions, (f) has enough time to talk every day as needed, (g) an encourager. I like the way Charles Stanley says it: "An accountability partner is able to perceive what you can't see when blind spots and weaknesses block your vision. Such a person serves as a tool in God's hand to promote spiritual growth, and he or she watches out for your best interest."

6. Commit to absolute honesty.

You must never lie to your accountability partner. The same holds true for your small group or recovery group. Relapse loves secrets. If you have a slip or struggle, you need to own it and say it. Stephen Covey writes, "Accountability breeds responsibility." This cannot be done apart from absolute honesty.

7. Develop a specific plan.

While this may seem tedious (it is!), plans trump non-plans every single time. Our exercise this week will focus on a plan, which we will offer to get you started. This plan needs to include specific, daily actions that you will take in order to maintain complete transparency, honesty, and accountability.

8. Use accountability software.

This is for the recovering addict. We recommend Covenant Eyes. While no tool is full proof, you should take advantage of modern technology. This will send a daily report to your accountability partner, telling him or her of any improper use of your devices. We always suggest that the person who receives these daily reports not be your spouse.

One More Thing

We will conclude with something you may not want to read. *You alone are responsible for your personal recovery.* We both know what it is to suffer trauma and abuse, but we have to own our response to that trauma and abuse. Steve Maraboli said it well: "The victim mindset dilutes the human potential. By not accepting personal responsibility for our circumstances, we greatly reduce our power to change them."

Dr. Denis Waitley writes, "There are two primary choices in life: to accept conditions as they exist, or accept the responsibility for changing them." You are not to blame for how you got here, but what you do next is on you. If you as a couple are to not only survive, but thrive, you must take responsibility for your personal health and then that of the marriage. As J.K. Rowling said, "There is an expiration date on blaming others."

THIS WEEK'S EXERCISE
Write it Out

We believe it is important for both spouses — the offender and the spouse — to be accountable to others, outside the marriage. Obviously, the level of accountability and the specific plan will be informed by each situation. The sex addict who has recently acted out will need an extra layer of accountability, whereas the wounded spouse's needs will be more along the lines of emotional support. The key is to write it out — a personal accountability plan that works best for you.

Elements to Your Plan

Some of the following elements will be a part of your personal accountability plan. Check the ones you think apply to your situation and specific needs.

- Covenant Eyes _____
- Accountable to You _____
- Give spouse all passcodes _____
- Let spouse view phone anytime _____
- Disclosure if requested _____
- Polygraph if requested _____
- 12-Step work _____
- Work with a sponsor _____
- Small group _____
- Weekly Recovery Night exercises with spouse _____
- Daily check-in with spouse _____
- Daily check-in with recovery ally_____
- Personal therapy _____
- Couples therapy _____
- Other: _____
- Other: _____
- Other: _____
- Other: _____

Now write out your plan, incorporating the items you checked from above.

_____

_____

_____

_____

_____

_____

_____

_____

_____

_____

_____

WEEK NINE

Relapse

One of the most horrific things a wounded spouse can hear is the news of her husband's relapse. Let us say something very important up front. Relapse is a process, not an event. There are signs; relapse doesn't just happen. It is imperative that the addict stay within his recovery plan every day. A missed meeting here and a misstep there can grow a snowball into an avalanche.

While every 12-Step meeting has stories of fresh relapses, it is critical that both the addict and the spouse understand this absolute truth — *relapse is not inevitable*. And we remind addicts that no matter the circumstances that led him to the precipice of relapse, he still has a choice in the moment. Relapse is a process and relapse is a choice.

Let's consider the story of a friend of the Apostle Paul. His story is tragic, but all too familiar.

Demas: The Great Relapser
2 Timothy 4:9-10

This is his story. In the final chapter of Paul's last letter, while addressing most of his remarks to Timothy, he took a moment to elude to the sad story of an old friend. "Do your best to come to me quickly, for Demas, because he loved this present world, has deserted me and he's gone to Thessalonica" (2 Timothy 4:9-10).

We get a glimpse into Demas' demise from the downward trajectory of his three brief references in Scripture. First, he was listed as a fellow-laborer with Paul (Philemon 1:24). Then he was simply referred to by name (Colossians 4:14). Then we read his spiritual obituary in our reading above. Demas — once a faithful servant — had forsaken the ministry because "he loved this present world." His was the story of spiritual degeneration, and his name has become synonymous with a deserter. We'll call him the great relapser.

What led to his relapse? We can't say for certain, but that won't keep us from offering a few theories.

1. It may be that Demas never fully counted the cost.

It is possible that Demas was swept into the church on a wave of emotion. The idea of sacrifice and imprisonment may not have set well with him. Similarly, many men and women relapse into their addictions because their sobriety was never particularly solid in the first place. We have seen it happen many times — a person embraces the *idea* of recovery, but never really engages the *work* of recovery.

2. The years may have worn him down.

One of my mentors, Dr. John Bisagno, used to say, "Only ten percent of us finish strong." Perhaps that was the story of Demas. Many years had passed from the days when he was a young servant to Paul until his final relapse.

There once lived a tramp named W.H. Davies, who went on to become a great poet. He caught a vision of his life's call at Tintern Abbey, a monastery in Wales. Twenty-seven years later, he returned to the same place in order to reflect on his life. He wrote, "As I stood there now, 27 years after, and compared that young boy's enthusiasm with my present lukewarm feelings, I was not very well pleased with myself."

Scholar William Barclay theorizes that this may have been the plight of Demas. His love for God may have slowly turned cold through the years. This is how many of us relapse. Remember, relapse is a process, not an event.

3. Demas may have simply chosen to relapse.

All we really know is that Demas made a choice. He knew what it was to live for God and he knew what it was to live for himself. He chose to trade in the former for the latter. "He loved this present world."

With Demas, we have more questions than answers. His name was the shortened version of Demetrius. Thus, this man may be the same Demetrius who led the riot of silversmiths at Ephesus where they sought to lynch Paul (Acts 19:25). He may have been the Demetrius of whom John wrote that he had a good report (3 John 1:12). The story of Demas' relapse into "this present world" may have been complex, with multiple examples of serving God intermingled with fits of rage and relapse.

That is how relapse works. We can be on track with our recovery, but become derailed by any number of things. If this once faithful servant of Paul was vulnerable to relapse, so are you and I.

Three Stages of Relapse

Let us repeat what we said earlier — relapse is a process, not an event. Relapse starts weeks or even months before the physical event. Generally, we (a) feel it, (b) think it, then (c) do it. We will refer to these three stages as emotional, mental, and physical.

1. Emotional Relapse

Dr. Steven Melemis writes, "In emotional relapse, you're not thinking about acting out. But your emotions and behaviors are setting you up for a possible relapse in the future." He identifies ten signs of an emotional relapse:

- Anxiety
- Intolerance
- Anger
- Defensiveness
- Mood swings
- Isolation
- Not asking for help
- Not going to meetings
- Poor eating habits
- Poor sleep habits

Emotional relapse is all about moods and feelings. These are somewhat related to middle circle behaviors in that they are not necessarily bad of themselves, but they can certainly lead to trouble. The answer is to practice self-regulation and self-awareness. We need to see the signs of relapse before we experience the full relapse itself.

2. Mental Relapse

With mental relapse, there is a war going on in the mind. This is the stage in which you find yourself battling fantasy and euphoric recall. If you are the spouse, mental relapse is tied to negative thinking, worry, and fears. With addiction relapse, we never do what we didn't think first. Here are a few signs of mental relapse:

- Thinking about former acting out partners or places
- Glamorizing the "old times"
- Lying
- Reconnecting with unhealthy relationships
- Spending more time on social media
- Staying up late to watch TV

- Planning out how we would act out if we did

Eventually, mental relapse leads to an inevitable conclusion. The key is to cut it off before our minds get too far down the road.

3. Physical Relapse

Once you feel it and think it, you are likely to do it. The key is to cut things off before you get to the physical relapse phase. This is the acting out phase, which constitutes a full relapse into your addiction. S.A. Tawks, in *Mule*, wrote, "I guess my biggest problem is that I find it easier to relapse than to carry through." This is the story of every addict who fails to stop himself before getting to the final phase.

A Proactive Plan

Wisdom plans for the possibility of relapse. I (Mark) warn addicts, "No matter how far you go down the road of recovery, the ditch is still just as close on either side." Every person in successful recovery should have a proactive plan in place, so he is ready when the circumstances and triggers line up against him. Following are a few examples of a proactive plan. These are beneficial for both the addict and his spouse.

1. Practice self-care.

The most important thing you can do to prevent a relapse is to take better care of yourself. Take a Recovery Day. Eat well, get exercise, and engage in healthy activities. Keep your spiritual connection strong and active. Love yourself before you try to love anyone else.

2. Play the tape through.

When you think about returning to your destructive ways, play the tape to the end, in your mind. Yes, acting out will bring relief and pleasure. But it will not end well. Remind yourself how the story ends — with disclosure, pain, and destruction. Remind yourself that even if you aren't "caught," you will feel guilt and shame. It never ends well.

3. Talk to someone.

When tempted, call a friend or sponsor. Share your struggles. Get them out. Sharing your temptations is magic. Just getting it out brings a connection with others, and you will benefit from their strength and hope. You will also be a blessing to them.

4. Take it one day at a time.

One of the things we suggest is that you (the addict) adopt this mantra: "I'm not saying I'll never act out again, but I am saying it won't be today." Don't think in terms of forever abstinence; think about the one day you know you have. Even for those in recovery for several years, it's the one day at a time attitude that gets them through.

5. Practice the 20-minute rule.

This is one of the most important things you can do when you feel relapse coming on. Most sexual urges pass within about 20 minutes. So have a 20-minute plan in place. Our ministry has produced tools that can help with this. Once you distract yourself for 20 minutes, the temptations will usually fade.

6. Spend time with positive people.

Chuck Swindoll says the two things that will determine the difference in where we are now versus where we will be in one year are the books we read and the people we spend time with. People will either lift you or bring you down. When you fill your life with people who are happy, positive, driven, and grounded, you will be far more likely to take on those traits yourself. You will become like those with whom you surround yourself, so choose wisely.

7. Do something new.

As long as it doesn't threaten your recovery, a new hobby or interest is a great way to keep yourself active, engaged, and healthy. In addiction, we often look back; recovery is about looking forward. As we often tell addicts, a big reason we get into trouble is that we aren't getting into anything else.

8. Get a dog.

We recommend West Highland Terriers! The point is, the company of a pet can help to even out our emotions and bring a fresh bond that feeds our recovery. Caring for a dog (or even a cat!) teaches unconditional love and provides incredible joy and activity.

Conclusion

Recovery expert Holli Kenley wrote, "Don't stay too long in the shame-filled grounds of relapse. Fertile soil awaits your return and your recovery."

While relapse is frequent, we repeat: it is not inevitable. You may have heard the well-known addiction saying, "Relapse is a part of recovery." Whoever said that is giving you bad advice. You don't have to relapse. In order to find success, you need to become proactive in your recovery. Deal with the things that keep taking you backward. The old philosopher Hippocrates said, "What remains in diseases after the crisis is apt to produce relapses."

We all have something that "remains in the disease" which needs our attention. The good news is that you can go where millions have gone before — into a life of recovery void of relapse. Learn the stages and get to know the signs. And always have a plan in place.

THIS WEEK'S EXERCISE
Relapse Prevention

The American Addiction Center reports that relapse rates range from 40 to 60 percent, depending on the nature of the addiction. A study by Armor Meshkoff found that only five percent of those who do not seek help from a professional or from a 12-Step group ever find sobriety. According to the Recovery Village, with alcohol abuse, of all who seek treatment, only 20 percent stay sober for a year. But for those who remain sober for two years, the success rate jumps to 60 percent.

We often tell clients that the reason people get into trouble is that they aren't getting into anything else. Avoiding relapse is really not about what you don't do (act out). It is about what you do (daily recovery work). And no matter how far you travel down the road to recovery, the ditch is still just as close on either side of that road. In order to avoid relapse, you must do two things: (a) plan your work, then (b) work your plan.

For the Spouse

While there is no guarantee that your husband (or wife) will never act out again, there are certain boundaries that can be put in place. The recovering sex addict will want to establish these guardrails, not only for his own sobriety, but to establish his commitment to recovery before his spouse. His relapse prevention plan needs to be whatever works for him. But his spouse will want to weigh in. And that's okay. If you are the wounded spouse, write down a few things that you'd like to see your partner do to ensure his enduring sobriety in order to avoid relapse.

1. _____
2. _____
3. _____
4. _____
5. _____

For the Addict

Sober is not well. It's a good start, but that's all it is. Relapse prevention is all about working an intentional recovery plan. Your sobriety tomorrow will be determined by what you do today. So you need a plan. Don't try to avoid relapse; focus on recovery, and relapse prevention will be the result.

Write down the elements of your recovery work that you will commit to, which will equip you to avoid relapse.

Daily activities

1. _____
2. _____
3. _____
4. _____
5. _____

Weekly activities

1. _____
2. _____
3. _____

Monthly activities

1. _____
2. _____
3. _____

WEEK TEN
Forgiveness

This may be a difficult chapter for the wounded spouse. To forgive a cheating spouse is a tall order. A commitment to restoring the marriage is not a commandment to the offended partner, but forgiveness is. Gandhi was right: "Forgiveness is a virtue of the brave." Forgiving her spouse may be the most courageous thing the offended partner will ever do.

It is not our position that every addict should expect to be welcomed back by his spouse. But the fact that you are reading this right now indicates a joint commitment to the marriage by you and your spouse. The good news is that there is hope. We find an example of that hope in the incredible story of marital infidelity followed by forgiveness, from an obscure couple who lived 2,800 years ago.

Hosea and Gomer
Hosea 1-3

There is no better example of marital forgiveness than this one. Hosea was a prophet during the reign of four different kings in the Old Testament, covering about 38 years in the 8th century B.C. Gomer is described as a "promiscuous woman" (Hosea 1:2), whom the Lord told Hosea to marry. While serving as an illustration of God's forgiveness toward us, this is a real story of a man and a woman in need of the gift of forgiveness.

This is that story.

God told Hosea to take Gomer as his wife.

The Lord told the prophet to take Gomer as his wife, identifying her as a woman who would be unfaithful from the start. Hosea did exactly as he was told. And things went rapidly downhill from there.

WEEK ELEVEN
Meetings

There is something about going to meetings that feeds our recovery. The AA "big book" says, "Go to meetings when you want to, and go to meetings when you don't want to" (p. 344). It didn't take long for the founders of Alcoholics Anonymous (Dr. Bob and Bill W.) to see the value of meetings. For 85 years they have kept meeting. Today, according to the BBC News, there are 115,326 AA groups meeting in 175 different countries. This includes 60,143 groups in the United States.

The following groups have all made meetings foundational for their programs: Sex Addicts Anonymous (SAA, founded 1977), Sexaholics Anonymous (SA, founded 1979), Spouse-Anonymous (S-Anon, founded 1987), Celebrate Recovery (CR, founded 1991). We are both committed to the value of meetings, which is one reason we wrote this workbook. The book is best utilized within the context of going to meetings.

Our Story

Mark's Story

It was 2012. I (Mark) attended my first 12-Step meeting. I didn't go back for over a year, for one basic reason — I wasn't all in. And there is nothing more miserable than attending recovery meetings when you aren't in recovery. I still remember a reading from that first meeting: "The measure we gave was the measure we got back." I got nothing from it because I gave nothing to it.

In late 2013 that all changed. Following my discovery, I got into recovery in a serious way. I began attending two meetings a week in the Houston area: Tuesday at 6:30 a.m. and Friday at noon. Sex Addicts Anonymous had become my lifeline. I often attended other meetings as well, on Monday night, Tuesday night, and Sunday night. I got a sponsor and began to work the Steps.

As I got into therapy and worked my recovery program, I observed something that has not been contradicted by anything I've learned since. You can go to meetings and still not be sober, but you can't get sober without going to meetings. I committed to attending two meetings per year for one year. That was seven years and 700 meetings ago. Obviously, I still attend meetings each week. Meetings remain an integral part of my recovery.

Beth's Story

I resisted going to any kind of support group meeting for a long time, for two reasons. First, I reasoned that Mark was the one with the problem, not me. He was the one who needed to go to meetings and get fixed. Then I would be okay. Second, the fear of his sexual addiction becoming known was an overwhelming burden I carried. For me to go to a meeting felt like a great risk.

The ongoing pain of suffering alone drove me to attend my first meeting. I entered the room filled with fear and anger — fear of being known and anger for having been put in this position. When it was time to introduce myself, I used only my middle name. The remainder of the meeting, I sat in silence as I fought back the tears. But something about those women's stories resonated with me, so I went back.

I continued going to meetings and soon discovered connection to be a key ingredient for healing. Later, I got a sponsor who helped me to focus on my own healing instead of obsessing over Mark's recovery. I realized that I could choose to get well regardless of his choices. I continue to attend a weekly meeting even though Mark has been on a solid path of recovery since 2013, and I believe I am a healthier person in all areas of my life as a result of these meetings.

The Biblical Model

"They persevered in listening to the apostles' teaching, in the fellowship, in the breaking of bread and in prayers. Awe was in every soul; and many signs and wonders were done by the apostles. All the believers were together and they were in the habit of selling their goods and possessions and of distributing them amongst all as each had need. Daily they continued with one accord in the Temple, and breaking bread from house to house they received their food with joy and in sincerity of heart; and they kept praising God and everyone liked them. Daily the Lord added to them those who were being saved" (Acts 2:42-47).

There is no better example of going to meetings than this one. We see eight things about this early church and their meetings.

1. It was a learning group.

The church was committed to learning from the first apostles every time they met. They were not content to just meet; they were there to learn. The same is true of a good recovery meeting.

2. It was a fellowship group.

The Bible says they were committed to the fellowship. There is something special about gathering each week with others who share our common cause of recovery. This fellowship is an integral part of our recovery.

3. It was a praying group.

They made prayer a big part of their weekly meetings. The same is true of most 12-Step groups, even those that are not Christ-centered. They often include the Serenity Prayer and the Lord's Prayer as a part of their agenda.

4. It was a reverent group.

The word used in the text is "awe." It carries the idea of respect and adoration. For the early believers, every time they gathered, they met with a sense of reverence and dignity. Every meeting was special.

5. It was a happening group.

The church saw "signs and wonders" consistently. In a healthy recovery group, stories of change and redemption are common. As men and women share their accounts of deliverance and freedom, others are inspired to achieve recovery for themselves.

6. It was a sharing group.

The early church shared their resources according to each person's needs. Under no compulsion, they were happy to help one another. Similarly, recovery groups are sensitive to each participant's needs.

7. It was a worshiping group.

Sure, they could have worshiped in private. But while God calls us into a personal relationship with him, no one is called into a private relationship with God. Good meetings find a way to worship God.

8. It was a happy group.

The word "gladness" comes to mind. The text says they were filled with gladness, not just touched by it. In recovery meetings, participants will often cheer aloud in celebration of the success of other members.

Components of a Good Meeting

Let us be clear. We are supportive of any meeting that feeds recovery. But not all meetings are created equal. While there is great value in the various 12-Step groups and other support groups that are available, our research and experience have convinced us that there are four components to the best weekly meetings.

1. Christ-centered

Most 12-Step programs have a spiritual foundation. Seven of the twelve Steps are spiritual in their verbiage. But we tell clients who claim a "higher power" other than Jesus Christ that they need to upgrade their higher power. God is the author of recovery; the best meetings are Christ-centered.

2. Solutions based

Many meetings consist of drunks telling other drunks how they got drunk. It is not enough to support and hear one another. The meetings need to lead men and women toward actual recovery. This requires material and formats that intentionally teach specific principles that lead to recovery.

3. Professionally led

Most 12-Step meetings are led by a facilitator, or "trusted steward." For some groups, this leader for the week must have 30 days of sobriety. Other groups require no sobriety at all. While these volunteers are well-suited for the format of these programs, they lack the training and experience of someone with degrees and certifications in the field of recovery.

4. Accountability-driven

One of the beautiful things about a successful meeting is that each participant is held accountable for his or her recovery. There are no casual observers. Each person checks in his or her recovery and commits to the program each week. Stephen Covey writes, "Accountability breeds responsibility." And Florence Nightingale said, "I think one's feelings waste themselves in words; they ought all to be distilled into actions which bring results."

Conclusion

The success of early church meetings did not guarantee their future. Just a few years after their first meetings (Acts 2), God's children had to be warned, "Let us consider how we may spur one another on toward love and good deeds, not giving up meeting together" (Hebrews 10:25). Meetings are a huge part of successful recovery — for the addict and the partner. I suppose there are stories of men and women who recovered without meetings; we just don't know of any.

THIS WEEK'S EXERCISE
Pick a Meeting

You need to be in a meeting, whether you are the addict or the spouse. Early in recovery, we recommend that the sex addict be in multiple meetings. These may include "secular" groups or Christ-centered groups. While in-person groups are best, Zoom meetings can be helpful, as well.

Check the group(s) you will attend.

There's Still Hope
- Freedom Group (men) _____
- Spouse Recovery Group (women) _____

Other Options
- Sexaholics Anonymous (men) _____
- Sex Addicts Anonymous (men) _____
- Celebrate Recovery (men and women) _____
- S-ANON (women) _____
- 180 Groups (men) _____
- Samson Society (men) _____

WEEK TWELVE
Recovery Fatigue

A great Welsh revival broke out in the 19th century. Not content to simply enjoy their faith, believers from Wales sent missionaries to far-reaching places across the globe. One of those places was India, in the region that is now part of the state of Meghalaya. It was there that these missionaries were met by the Garo head-hunting tribe.

The first convert to Christianity was a man who had a wife and two children. When the pagan tribal chief heard of his conversion, he was outraged, and immediately called on the man to recant his story of conversion. The man stood firm in his new faith. So the chief threatened to shoot arrows through his body, as well as through his wife and children, unless he denied Christ.

The man and his family refused to denounce their faith, so their execution was ordered. With their dying breath, the four of them lay on the ground singing a song whose origin remains unknown to this day. These are the words these martyrs sang:

"I have decided to follow Jesus.
I have decided to follow Jesus.
I have decided to follow Jesus.
No turning back, no turning back.

"Though none go with me, I still will follow.
Though none go with me, I still will follow.
Though none go with me, I still will follow.
No turning back, no turning back."

In 1958 an Australian named William J. Reynolds discovered these words on an old manuscript. A third stanza was added and that hymn can now be found in at least 56 hymnals.

Since the days when he walked the earth, millions of men and women have decided to follow Jesus. It's the "no turning back" part that trips so many of us up.

The same is true of recovery. By our estimate, looking back over the hundreds of recovery meetings we have attended, we have come to know at least 100 men and women who have started down the road to recovery, but looked back, retreated, and eventually dropped out. Many have suffered from what we call recovery fatigue. In fact, we believe that all who have done the hard work of recovery have struggled with recovery fatigue at some point, on some level.

Three Men — Three Excuses
Luke 9:57-62

Samuel Johnson said, "Great works are performed not by strength but by perseverance." The story of Luke 9 lays out a perfect example of that. For so many couples in recovery, there are waves of despair. This should be expected. There will be times when the husband, wife, or both just want to give up. The fight is too hard, the process too long, and the work too intensive. They suffer from recovery fatigue.

In this story, Jesus gave examples of three men who were each well-intentioned. And on the surface, no one could fault them for turning back. But in each case, Jesus said they should have kept going. Let's look at each man.

Man #1 — Inconsiderate Impulse

"As they were walking along the road, a man said to Jesus, 'I will follow you wherever you go.' Jesus replied, 'Foxes have dens and birds have nests, but the Son of Man has no place to lay his head'" (Luke 9:57-58).

This guy seemed to have it together. No excuses. All in. No turning back. But Jesus knew his heart. He knew that when he reminded the man that they would be spending each night outdoors or in a borrowed room, the man might reconsider the strength of his commitment. What Jesus was saying to him was, "Think before you commit. Count the cost. The work ahead will require lasting commitment, not an impulse."

Man #2 — Conflicting Duties

"He said to another man, 'Follow me.' But he replied, 'Lord, first let me go and bury my father.' Jesus said to him, 'Let the dead bury their own dead, but you go and proclaim the kingdom of God'" (Luke 9:59-69).

Well, this certainly seems harsh . . . until we understand the context. In biblical times, the death of one's father represented a time of transition. When a son buried his father, he was then free to pursue his own dreams. There is no evidence in the story to suggest the man's father was dead yet. In fact, if he had been, the man would have been back home, not walking the road with friends. So what the man was saying was, "I have my life to live first. When the time comes that a new way of life becomes more convenient, I'm all in." To the contrary, Jesus was looking for men and women who were ready to pursue him immediately. In recovery, it is natural to want to put off the hard work, but the time to begin is now.

Man #3 — Divided Mind

"Still another said, 'I will follow you, Lord; but first let me go back and say goodbye to my family.' Jesus replied, 'No one who puts a hand to the plow and looks back is fit for service in the kingdom of God'" (Luke 9:61-62).

Jesus knew the man's heart. He knew that if this guy had returned to his family, he would probably stay there. Following Christ — and pursuing recovery — require looking forward, not back. Jesus likened it to a man plowing his field. It is impossible to plow a straight furrow while looking back over our shoulder. One commentary says it like this: "Plowing a field requires an eye intent on the furrow to be made. It is marred the instant one turns back. We see here a distracted attention and a divided heart." Dr. Albert Barnes wrote of this passage, "It must be all or nothing. Give up the good for the better."

How to Overcome Recovery Fatigue

Coach Lou Holtz was right: "You aren't going to find anybody that's going to be successful without making a sacrifice and without perseverance." In order for recovery to be successful, individually and as a couple, we must commit to the process — fatigue or not. We have found six practical principles that help to overcome recovery fatigue.

1. Practice self-care.

This is the one most of us underestimate. But we can be no good to our spouse if we aren't first good to ourselves. Eat healthy meals. Get plenty of exercise. Engage in a hobby. Do things for yourself. Do the same thing as a couple. Don't make everything about recovery. Take in a movie, try a new restaurant, and do something fun.

2. Keep your eye on the prize.

You can overcome the present if you look to the future. It is when we focus on what is happening now that we miss what is coming later. Never judge yourself by your worst day. When times are hard and recovery is difficult, keep going, with an eye on the prize.

3. Don't walk this journey alone.

You need a climbing partner. This needs to be a friend of the same sex who is willing to walk this journey with you. Preferably, this should be someone who is on the road to recovery themselves. There's an old saying, "It's lonely at the top. " In couples work, you will never get to the top if you are lonely. You need someone else to join you along the way.

4. Remind yourselves of the benefits of recovery.

When fatigue kicks in, remind yourselves that it is worth it. Sing the words to the song at the start of this lesson: "No turning back, no turning back." Remind yourselves that you have come too far to turn back now. For those who endure through the hard times, there is a reward you can't imagine.

5. Celebrate the process, not just the goal.

Enjoy the journey. Recovery is all about direction, not destination. There is no graduation ceremony for recovery. You don't finish the course. You remain a work in progress. So enjoy recovery activities together. Enjoy life together. Enjoy the meetings, the therapy, reading recovery books, and climbing the mountain — one step at a time.

6. Take a break.

You don't climb a mountain with a burst. You need a break from time to time. It's okay to miss a 12-Step meeting once in a while. It's okay to not always be in therapy. It's okay to not make recovery the central topic of every conversation. Go on a trip, take in a game, do something fun. If you go 100% all the time, you'll wear out. So take an occasional break.

Conclusion

The year was 1972. The Summer Olympics were held in Munich, West Germany. American Frank Shorter won the gold medal in the marathon, with a time of 2 hours, 12 minutes. But that same year, there was another race being held — at Sharpstown Junior High School in Houston, Texas. I (Mark) was there.

It was a one-mile run, featuring the boys of my seventh grade class. And halfway around the first lap, there I was — all alone in first place. For 13-year-old kids, a mile run might as well have been the marathon in Munich. Coach Gascamp told us to pace ourselves. And every runner listened, except me.

What was I doing in first place? It was simple. There was a girl in the stands, watching us run. Kristina was the girl of my dreams. Intent on impressing her, I set out to sprint the entire mile, setting a new world's record. But as

I extended my lead, I did something really dumb. I looked back. Was Kristina watching me? I had to know.

At that point, I tripped over my own feet and tumbled to the ground. I got up just in time to finish the race in last place.

Recovery is a marathon. No one wins the prize on the first lap. For most of us, it seems impossible at some point. We can relate to the words of Nelson Mandela: "It always seems impossible until it's done."

Recovery fatigue. It's a real threat to the progress of every couple. But if we push through it, the rewards are well worth the pain.

THIS WEEK'S EXERCISE
Fatigue Control

It is important that you not become weary in well-doing. You need a recovery plan for yourself and for your marriage. We hope this exercise will help. Do the first part on your own and the second part with your husband or wife. Then do the third part on your own.

Part 1: Your Personal Recovery Plan

Write out the things you will include in our own recovery plan. Elements might include 12-Step meetings, sponsor work, Step work, coaching or group work with us at There's Still Hope, reading recovery materials, getting on Covenant Eyes, an accountability partner, spiritual disciplines, daily exercise, healthy diet, meditation, journaling, therapy, podcasts, retreats, and more. Things you will do daily:

- _____
- _____
- _____
- _____
- _____
- _____
- _____
- _____
- _____
- _____

Things you will do weekly or monthly:

- _____
- _____
- _____
- _____

Part 2: Your Couples Recovery Plan

- _____
- _____
- _____
- _____
- _____
- _____
- _____
- _____

Part 3: How You Will Keep Things Fresh

- _____
- _____
- _____
- _____
- _____
- _____

WEEK THIRTEEN
Church

The story is told of the night evangelist Dwight L. Moody visited a man in his home, who insisted that while he needed God, he didn't need the church. The man told his story as they sat in his living room, which was kept warm by the fire in his fireplace. After a few minutes, not saying a word, Moody got up and moved toward the fireplace. He took a tool from the mantle, and gently removed a single coal from the fire and set it aside. Within a few minutes, that coal had gone dark. The homeowner understood the message of the cooling coal. Apart from the rest of the coals, its fire would go out.

The same is true of the church. Think of it like this. While God calls each of us to a *personal* relationship with his Son, he doesn't call any of us to a *private* relationship with his Son.

The Bible warns, "Do not forsake the assembling of yourselves together" (Hebrews 10:25). The theme of community and gathering is dominant throughout Scripture.

"One Another" Passages of the Bible

Scripture traces the theme of unity and gathering together from the beginning of time. Consider the following examples of God's children being identified as "one another."

Theme of Unity

About a third of the "one another" commands of Scripture focus on the church getting along in unity.

- Be at peace with one another (Mark 9:30).
- Don't grumble against one another (John 6:43).
- Be of the same mind with one another (Romans 12:6).
- Accept one another (Romans 15:7).
- Wait for one another (1 Corinthians 11:33).

- Don't consume one another (Galatians 5:15).
- Don't envy one another (Galatians 5:26).
- Be patient with one another (Ephesians 4:2).
- Forgive one another (Colossians 3:13).
- Seek good for one another (1 Thessalonians 5:15).
- Don't complain against one another (James 4:11).
- Confess sins to one another (James 5:16).

Theme of Love

Another third of the "one another" passages deal with love. Here are a few examples.

- Love one another (John 13:34).
- Through love, serve one another (Galatians 5:13).
- Tolerate one another in love (Ephesians 4:2).
- Greet one another with a kiss of love (1 Peter 5:14).
- Be devoted to one another in love (Romans 12:10).

Theme of Humility

Another 15 percent of the "one another" passages center on humility.

- Wash one another's feet (John 13:14).
- Give preference to one another (Romans 12:10).
- Serve one another (Galatians 5:13).
- Be subject to one another (Ephesians 5:21).
- Regard one another as important (Philippians 2:3).
- Clothe yourselves in humility toward one another (1 Peter 5:5).

Miscellaneous "One Another" Passages

- Don't judge one another (Romans 14:13).
- Bear one another's burdens (Galatians 6:2).
- Speak truth to one another (Ephesians 4:25).
- Don't lie to one another (Colossians 3:9).
- Comfort one another (1 Thessalonians 4;18).
- Encourage one another (1 Thessalonians 5:11).
- Pray for one another (James 5:16).
- Be hospitable to one another (1 Peter 4:9).

The Original 120
Acts 1:15

"At a time when about 120 disciples had gathered together, Peter got up and spoke to them" (Acts 1:15). And with that, the church was off and running.

The 120 would quickly swell to 5,000 by the end of Acts 2. By Acts 13, the church was sending out missionaries across the known world, which would eventually result in taking the Good News to America. But it all began with the 120.

There is significance to the number 120. Since there were about 4 million Jews in Palestine, that means that only one in 30,000 were Christians. By that standard, the city of Dallas would have about 40 Christ followers. The three Texas cities we served as pastor/wife would have very few believers: Friendswood (1), Gainesville (1), and Conroe (2). Yet, these early believers would go on to change the world in the span of a single generation.

The number 120 had been significant in Scripture long before the Book of Acts. In 2 Chronicles, the story is told of 120 priests who performed the act of purification at the dedication of the Temple (2 Chronicles 6:1-18). The 120 lifted their trumpets and voices to God in power and unity.

In like manner, the 120 followers of Christ gathered to hear God's Word, to worship, and then be a part of the Day of Pentecost, which would change everything. The Church has been meeting every Sunday for over 2,000 years since then, never missing a single Sunday.

Connection of Church to Recovery

Although we don't know of any studies specific to the role of church in strengthening recovery per se, several studies leave clear implications. For example, Brian and Melissa Grim cite a study that concludes that 73 percent of addiction treatment programs in America include a faith-based element. A Duke University study cited hundreds of evidence-based studies that demonstrate a link between faith and mental well-being. A study by Lyons et al. (2010) found that 82 percent of clients who experienced a spiritual awakening during recovery were completely abstinent one year later, compared with 55 percent of those who had no such spiritual connection.

Benefits of Going to Church

Our purpose here is not to construct a compelling case for church broadly. That is for another time and place. Because our interest is in recovery, we will confine our comments to the benefits of a living church connection as it applies to recovery. We see several ways in which this seems to be true.

2. We must turn to God in desperate times (3:3-4).

David begins the third verse with two profound words: "But you." This reflects a shift in focus. He goes on to describe God as his (a) shield, (b) glory, (c) restorer of joy, and (d) first responder. Billy Graham said it like this: "The Christian life is not a constant high. I have my moments of deep discouragement. I have to go to God in prayer with tears in my eyes and say, 'O God, forgive me,' or 'Help me.'" Every addict and spouse can resonate with those words.

3. In desperation we find peace (3:5-6).

After he cried out to God, David went to bed — not in the palace, but in the wilderness. He slept through the night. Despite his enemies closing in, David slept. Despite his personal shame, David slept. With no regard for the worrisome events of the coming day, David slept. Sometimes, the addict — and especially the spouse — want sleep more than anything else. Sleep represents peace. This can only come from God.

4. We learn to depend only on God (3:7-8).

You won't realize that God is all you need until God is all you have. For King David, that day had come. David's closing words to the psalm were robust: "Salvation belongs to the Lord. Your blessing be upon your people." In other words, David was not depending on his troops, wealth, or personal wisdom. He would not defeat Absalom or return to the throne unless God came through.

Mother Teresa said, "Prayer is not asking. Prayer is putting oneself in the hands of God, at his disposition, and listening to his voice in the depth of our hearts." For the couple in recovery, prayer is a turning point. In prayer, we recognize that all the recovery work in the world, accompanied by the finest therapy and human support will fall short, unless we rely on the God of the universe. As Mother Teresa said, "Prayer is putting oneself in the hands of God." Nothing more, nothing less.

Seven Components of Couples Prayer

There is no template for how to pray for your recovery and for that of your marriage. Although we can certainly glean certain principles from Scripture and the thousands of volumes written by experts in the field, there is no simple outline to follow when praying in this area. We will keep this simple, by offering seven components of prayer for couples in recovery. You can — and should — add to this list.

1. Repentance

"Repent therefore, and turn again, that your sins may be blotted out" (Acts 3;19).

2. Strength

"My soul is weary with sorrow; strengthen me according to your word" (Psalm 119:28).

3. Intercession

"Therefore, confess your sins to one another and pray for one another, that you may be healed" (James 5:16).

4. Thanksgiving

"With praise and thanksgiving they sang to the Lord" (Ezra 3:11).

5. Forgiveness

"Forgive us our debts, as we also have forgiven our debtors" (Matthew 6:12).

6. Resentments

"Bearing with one another and, if one has a complaint against another, forgiving each other, as the Lord has forgiven you, so you must also forgive" (Colossians 3:13).

7. Hope

"And your life will be brighter than the noonday; its darkness will be like the morning. And you will feel secure, because there is hope; you will look around and take your rest in security" (Job 11:17-19).

Three Daily Prayers

As part of my own recovery (Mark's), I repeat three prayers every day — at least three times. This is something I learned from the world's greatest sponsor (mine) over five years ago. It is a habit from which I never deviate. It keeps me grounded and focused. We suggest these prayers be added to your daily routine, as well.

Third Step Prayer

"God, I offer myself to you, to build with me and do with me as you will. Relieve me of the bondage of self, that I may better do your will. Take away my difficulties, that victory over them may bear witness to those I would help of your power, your love, and your way of life."

Seventh Step Prayer

"My Creator, I am now willing that you should have all of me, good and bad. I pray that you now remove from me every single defect of character which stands in the way of my usefulness to you and to my fellows. Grant me strength as I go out from here, to do your bidding."

Serenity Prayer

"God, grant me the serenity to accept the things I cannot change, the courage to change the things I can, and the wisdom to know the difference."

A Final Word

Let us leave you with a final word about prayer. Before prayer becomes a part of your recovery, it needs to be a part of your life. Charles Spurgeon defined prayer: "True prayer is neither a mere mental exercise nor a vocal performance. It is far deeper than that. It is a spiritual transaction with the Creator of heaven and earth."

We must become men and women of prayer as a preventative measure. Too often we run to God to bail us out, rather than to simply commune with him. Corrie ten Boom posed, "Is prayer your steering wheel or your spare tire?" Prayer needs to be your steering wheel. Kierkegaard said the mature believer prays, not in order that things may change, but so that he may change. May each of us adopt that posture in our prayer lives, for the sake of recovery and for the sake of our marriages.

THIS WEEK'S EXERCISE
Prioritizing Prayer

The disciples had this request of the Master: "Teach us to pray." Note, they didn't ask Jesus to teach them how to pray, but to *just pray*. Jesus was a man of prayer, rising up early in the morning to pray in the mountain (Mark 1:35). Jesus prayed in the Garden (John 17), from the cross (Luke 23), and with the disciples (Matthew 11). Jesus prayed before raising Lazarus (John 11) and upon entering Jerusalem (John 12). Jesus was a man of prayer.

If you are to establish a priority of prayer, this will mean committing to three things: a plan, a place, and a pattern.

Plan

You need to establish a specific plan for your prayer life. Otherwise, prayer will be crowded out by more immediate things that will pop up in your daily schedule. This requires nailing down a time when you will pray every time.

Your plan/time:

_____

Pattern

How will you pray? There are many ways. You can "freelance," praying in the moment. You can pray off of a prayer list. I (Mark) suggest that those in recovery pray the 3rd Step Prayer, the 7th Step Prayer, and the Serenity Prayer three times every day. You might try the ACTS formula for prayer, which means praying in four areas: (a) adoration, (b) confession, (c) thanksgiving, and (d) supplication.

Your pattern:

_____

_____

Place

The Bible always tells us Jesus' location when he prayed: mountain, garden, tomb, cross, etc. It is good to have a specific place for daily prayer. This may be in your home or office, or it might even be another place such as a park. Establish a place for daily prayer.

Your place:

_____

WEEK FIFTEEN
Signs of Trouble

From 1955 until her death in 2000, Ann Landers wrote an advice column that was read by 90 million people at one point. Her work won her recognition as the most influential woman in the United States, according to the 1978 *World Almanac*. When asked for wisdom on hundreds of subjects, her most common response was this: "Expect trouble as an inevitable part of life and repeat to yourself, the most comforting words of all — this too shall pass."

No one has ever done recovery work perfectly. For the addict, the spouse, and the couple, the journey is marked by difficulties, doubts, and detours. The good news is that it gets better with time, if both partners keep their recovery on track.

There is no magic timeline for successful recovery. Relapse can happen any time. But there are signs of trouble, if you know what to look for. We will discuss those signs this week. First, let's review the three simple stages of relapse.

Three Stages of Relapse

Although it is certainly possible for the spouse of the addict to relapse in her recovery, for our purposes here, our focus will be on the addict. When we think of relapse or trouble, we usually think of the addict slipping back into his old ways. But before he acts out with his body, he will act out with his mind. And there are signs of trouble, if his wife knows what to look for. These signs show up in each of these three states of relapse.

Stage 1 — Emotional

The first state of relapse involves shifting moods and inconsistent reactions to life. The addict usually becomes depressed and withdrawn. He pulls back from reality. Feelings of loss and loneliness give way to thoughts of fantasy. Self-medication is not far behind.

Stage 2 — Mental

Before a man acts out with a woman in his bed, he does so in his head. The transition from an emotional slip to a mental slip can be instantaneous. In mental relapse, the addict plans his next sexual encounter, whether it is with porn, a live person, or just himself. He plays out the event in his mind, with attention to every detail.

Stage 3 — Physical

Once the relapse reaches the physical stage, the addict is no longer in recovery. By acting out with himself, another person, or an image, he has moved back into his addiction. The signs of this activity should be fairly obvious.

Peter's Denial — Signs It Was Coming
Mark 14:66-72

As predicted by Jesus, Peter denied him three times. The story is familiar, but worth repeating.

The Biblical Account

"While Peter was below in the courtyard, one of the servant girls of the high priest came by. When she saw Peter warming himself, she looked closely at him. 'You also were with that Nazarene, Jesus,' she said.

"But he denied it. 'I don't know or understand what you're talking about,' he said, and went out into the entryway.

"When the servant girl saw him there, she said again to those standing around, 'This fellow is one of them.' Again he denied it.

"After a little while, those standing near said to Peter, 'Surely you are one of them, for you are a Galilean.'

"He began to call down curses, and he swore to them, 'I don't know this man you're talking about.'

"Immediately the rooster crowed the second time. Then Peter remembered the word Jesus had spoken to him: 'Before the rooster crows twice, you will disown me three times.' And he broke down and wept."

Sign #1 — Self-confidence

Peter was sure of himself. He would fight for Christ to the death. He said there was no way he would ever deny Jesus. The same is true of many addicts. "I'll never act out again," they say. And they mean it. But self-confidence often gives way to self-indulgence.

Sign #2 — Lack of prayer

Instead of praying with Jesus in the Garden, Peter was found sleeping. He wasn't thinking about how he needed God's help. Even though the Lord had warned him to watch and pray, Peter slept on the job. Confidence in self brings slumber in all areas – including recovery.

Sign #3 — Not following God's Word

Peter tried to fight the arresting officers, despite Jesus' warning. Jesus had to tell him to put away his sword – after he had done great damage. As Christians, we must be committed to learning, and following God's Word. It is natural to dive into recovery materials, and that is a good thing. But we must never stray from the Word of God.

Sign #4 — Hanging with the wrong crowd

Peter was standing with people outside the house instead of with the disciples who were encouraging one another. In his isolation from fellow believers, he fell. This is a reliable sign of trouble. When you find your addict husband spending more time with his old buddies than his recovery circle, you are right to be alarmed.

Sign #5 — Return to old habits

Peter's language slipped. He began cursing, a sign of a return to his old ways. When you see your husband acting like he did when he was stuck in his addiction, take note. Even subtle hints of a return to old habits can be meaningful.

Indications Your Spouse Is in Trouble

Again, our focus here is on the husband as the likely addict. The spouse sees signs of trouble with his recovery, but isn't sure if (a) the signs are real, or (b) she should say anything. We'll save the "say anything" part for another day (the short answer is "yes"), as our focus here will be the signs themselves. Here is a list of the things you might watch for.

1. Gaslighting

The gaslighter will say whatever is necessary to take the focus off of himself. The cheating spouse may even accuse his spouse of being the cheater, to keep her on the defensive. Writing for *Psychology Today*, Dr. Stephanie Sarkis summarized the gaslighter: "The goal is to keep you so busy defending yourself and being emotionally distraught that you don't have enough time to pay attention to his own behavior."

2. Withdrawn

It's normal for a marriage to get to a point that you aren't communicating as much as you used to, but if your spouse becomes uncommonly withdrawn, this can be a sign of trouble. Sometimes, the addict feels he is not being heard, or his interests are not being appreciated by his wife. His response may be to turn inward, and to eventually look for self-medication in all the wrong ways.

3. Lack of intimacy

Sexual attraction has faded, and your spouse no longer seems interested in you or your advances. Although this could be due to many things, this can certainly be a sign of trouble. If your husband is consistently rejecting you in the bedroom, he may be seeking sexual pleasure in other ways.

4. Disrespectful

It is not uncommon for the addict to show a reduction of interest in his wife's priorities when he is slipping in his recovery. Because he is sliding through the three stages of relapse, he doesn't have the time or energy to connect with his wife. The signs are subtle, but real.

5. Cell phone defense

This may be the surest sign of trouble there is. When the addict begins to protect his phone like it's the Hope diamond, that usually means there is something worth hiding. When the addict never sets his phone down or hands it to his wife to use, there is almost always a problem.

6. Social media

Facebook can be an addiction of its own. When the addicted spouse is on social media a lot, he may be looking up pictures of women acquaintances or of women in his past. He may be following their daily activities and posts, with an unhealthy interest in someone other than his spouse. We often suggest the addict get off social media for at least one year in early recovery.

7. Private calls

A real sign of trouble is when the addict consistently steps out of the room (or house) to take phone calls. When he does this for business purposes, he should show his wife evidence of who called immediately after the call. And the spouse should be given 100 percent access to his phone at all times, without him making her out to be a nag.

8. Missing money

It usually starts small. Just $5 or $10 missing can be a sign of trouble. We suggest the addict keep no more than $20 on him at any time, unless he is traveling. (Even then, he doesn't need to carry a lot of cash.) When he does spend cash, he should always keep receipts.

9. Defensiveness

It's never easy for the spouse to question her husband's fidelity. They should have an agreement, hammered out early in recovery. Anytime the wife has a question, she should be able to ask it without repercussion. A defensive posture is a huge warning sign.

10. Diminished recovery work

One of the surest signs of trouble is missed recovery meetings. Although it is common for an addict to require fewer 12-Step meetings to maintain solid recovery after three of four years, missed meetings, fewer recovery calls, and not reading recovery material all add up to trouble. The spouse whose husband no longer values recovery work has every right to be concerned.

THIS WEEK'S EXERCISE
Identify the Signs

We will offer a separate exercise for each partner. For the recovering sex addict, there is a critical need for him to stay on guard, to avoid the things that lead to a slip or relapse. For his spouse, she is wise to be aware of the signs that her spouse's recovery is not on track. After finishing your exercise, share your results with your spouse.

For the Sex Addict

It is our position that there is no such thing as a "fall." What leads to relapse can better be called a "slide." We get into trouble incrementally, one small step at a time. The person in recovery needs to stay diligent and follow a strict recovery plan. For this exercise, as you sit here right now, give yourself a grade, from "A" to "F" on how you are doing in each of the following areas. For any element of recovery that you feel you do not need to be engaged with right now, leave it blank. For the sake of our language, we will assume the addict is a male.

Daily devotions _____
Attending recovery meetings _____
Healthy diet _____
Working a specific recovery program _____
Protection of electronic devices _____
12-Step work _____
Physical exercise _____
Working with my sponsor _____
No hidden cash _____
No hidden texting with women _____
Personal therapy _____
Church involvement _____
Working on other addictions _____
Plenty of sleep _____
Praying recovery prayers _____
Monthly Recovery Day _____
Date night with wife _____
Sponsoring or mentoring other men _____
Personal accountability _____
Reading recovery materials _____

For the Spouse

What are the things you value most? How do you think your husband is doing in each of these areas? Check any areas that you see as a concern. For those that don't apply, leave them blank. Again, for the sake of language and brevity, we will assume the spouse is a woman.

Over-confidence _____
Lack of spiritual disciplines _____
Not active in church _____
Overly moody _____
Hanging out with the wrong crowd _____
Return to old habits _____
Not attending recovery meetings _____
Not doing recovery work _____
Overly defensive _____
Hidden devices _____
Gaslighting _____
Disrespectful _____
Hidden cash _____
Struggling with other addictions _____
Questionable social media _____

Private texting or calls _____
Defensiveness _____

WEEK SIXTEEN
Talking to Your Kids

In her groundbreaking book, *How to Talk So Kids Will Listen*, Adele Faber wrote, "I was a wonderful parent before I had children." We can relate. We were model parents for the first seven years of our marriage. Friends and neighbors commented on how well-groomed, sweet-natured, and compliant our seven-year-old was. In all modesty, they were right. Duffy was one of the most obedient and adoring cocker spaniels you can imagine.

Then we had a son. In our unbiased estimation, David was a perfect son and is a perfect young man, now in his 30s. But along the way, he has taught us more than we have taught him.

Statesman Frederick Douglass was right when he said, "It is easier to build strong children than to repair broken men." Sadly, porn and sex addiction have made both tasks very difficult. Every couple who has walked through the process of recovery has wrestled with challenging questions.

- What do we tell our kids?
- When do we tell them?
- What do we include and what do we leave out?

Because our addiction has affected our children, we need to talk to them. There is no template for how this works, and it is certainly not our intent to create one. There are as many ways to tell our children about our disease as there are children to tell. Although we will leave the details to you, God, and your family to navigate, we can offer principles we think will be helpful.

Abraham, Isaac, and Jacob
Genesis 12-26

Let's begin our discussion with a look at the most significant family of the Old Testament. In his inspiring article, *Four Important Parenting Lessons Straight from the Bible,* David Peach offers the example of the patriarch family that be-gan with Abraham. This is a great example of parenting. The Book of Genesis chronicles the family of Abraham through Joseph, his great-grandson. We can see four lessons from this amazing story, starting with Abraham.

Lesson #1 — Be a good role model.

We've all said it as parents. "Do as I say, not as I do." But the fact is, your child will follow your example, not your advice. The lying that Abraham did was copied by his son Isaac (Genesis 12:10-20, 26:7-11). The manipulation of Jacob was seen in Judah, his son (Genesis 27). Being a role model for your chil-dren — no matter their age – is really not a suggestion. It is a fact. The question is not whether you are a role model, but what kind of role model you are.

It is too late to go back and create a new past, but you can still create a new future. Be the right role model in how you address your struggles with your kids. Be honest. Be transparent. Be authentic. Be Christlike.

Lesson #2 — Be unified.

Never should one parent disclose the addiction by himself. Isaac and Re-bekah did many things right in their parenting, but one incredibly wrong thing they did was to be divided in their loyalties to their children. Isaac loved Esau more than Jacob, while Rebekah loved Jacob more than Esau (Genesis 25:27-28). Lack of unity within the couple led to all kinds of problems for their kids.

In talking to your children about your porn or sex issues, it is imperative that you do so as husband and wife, committed to each other, the marriage, and your children. They need to see you as one, committed to the future to-gether. Anything less will plant seeds of doubt that will create immense con-fusion and pain.

Lesson #3 — Demonstrate a spiritual connection.

Isaac had a clear understanding of who God was, based on everything that he learned from Abraham. We see Isaac trusting in the promises that God had given Abraham. In contrast, Jacob seemed to have a poor relationship with his children. After Joseph's brothers lied about Joseph being dead, they pretended to comfort their father Jacob (Genesis 37:35). If they really had the kind of re-lationship with him that was healthy, they would have never done the things they did.

In talking to our kids about our struggles with porn or sex addiction, we should demonstrate an intimate walk with God, as well as fostering an open and intimate relationship with each other and our children. Relationship trumps what we say every time. We have seen numerous examples of families in which children were told of their parent's addiction (usually dad's), and the one thing that preserved the family was the spiritual connections that had been built over the years.

Lesson #4 — Provide training.

When God came to Isaac to reiterate the Abrahamic covenant in Genesis 26, Isaac would have known all about the promise of God. Isaac was an integral part of that promise. In Genesis 22, Isaac was taught by Abraham and was well aware of what God had done in providing a sacrifice to take Isaac's place on the altar.

What to Tell Your Kids

Let's get specific. Disclosing our sex addiction or that of our spouse's is never easy, especially to our children. Dr. Buddy Janssen writes, "Dealing with the chaos and unpredictability of their home life, children can receive inconsistent messages." Janssen continues, "Children can feel guilty and shame trying to keep the family secrets. Often, they feel abandoned due to the emotional unavailability of their parents."

The challenge becomes breaking the silence without breaking our children in the process. We know that secrets almost never remain secrets. Our children will learn of our indiscretions and addictive behaviors; the key is for that to happen in a controlled way. Disclosure may lead to challenges for our kids in the areas of self-esteem, attachment, autonomy, and trust. When we talk to our children about these sensitive subjects, we owe it to them to get it right.

We offer the following five messages to communicate in disclosure to our children.

Message #1 — Addiction is a disease.

It is important for the couple (especially the addict's spouse) to tell their children that the addict isn't a bad person seeking to become good, but that he is a sick person seeking to get well. Addiction is a disease, not a choice. It is the predictable result of (a) trauma, (b) abuse, and (c) isolation. None of this excuses the addict's choices or behavior. But the nature of addiction as a disease must be underscored for the children.

Message #2 — It's not your fault.

The parents would never imagine that their children might think otherwise. But it is natural for our kids to try to own our mistakes. They must understand that they are not the reason a parent does anything he does. They did not cause the problem, nor can they fix it.

- Jigsaw puzzle
- Concerts/new bands
- Collecting shells
- Hiking
- Movie marathon
- Parasailing
- Reading a book together
- Board games
- Home improvement projects
- Skydiving
- Camping
- New hobby
- Car show

Nailing It Down

You have your marching orders. Draw from the story of Jacob and Rachel. Consider the previous list of possibilities for new experiences. Do the following exercise. Engage the process.

Walt Disney said, "We keep moving forward, opening new doors, and doing new things, because we're curious and curiosity keeps leading us down new paths." When a marriage has been afflicted by addiction, doing new things is not easy. We are more comfortable retreating to the familiarity of the anchors of our past. But Neale Donald Walsch was right: "Life begins at the end of your comfort zone." So get out of your comfort zone. Try some new experiences together as a couple. You both deserve it.

THIS WEEK'S EXERCISE
Name that Experience

This will be a two-parter. You and your partner will nail down some new places to go and new things to do as a couple. The key is that these experiences be something you have not done together in the past. Focus on a few "big things," of which you may do just two or three in the next 12 months. Then pick several things you can do together that are less expensive and easier to pull off. You should try to do several of these throughout the year. After you compile your lists, put some of these on your calendar, to be sure you make them happen.

Something Big

Select two or three things to do from this list. You will likely want to create your own experience.

Vacation to a new destination: _____
Overnight trip to a place within a few hours, where you have never been:
_____
Something special for your anniversary: _____
A weekend spiritual retreat together: _____
Take dance classes together: _____
Visit a state park (name it): _____
Do something scary (name it): _____
Visit a historic church (name it): _____

Less Expensive, Easier to Do

- Spend a night looking through your wedding album: _____
- Take dance lessons together: _____
- Movie marathon: _____
- Cook dinner together: _____
- Visit a nursing home together on Christmas: _____
- Overnight camping: _____
- Share a hobby experience: _____
- Hiking: _____
- New restaurant (name it): _____
- Car show: _____
- Visit a church of a different denomination: _____
- Art museum: _____
- Miniature golf: _____
- Real golf: _____
- Walk on the beach: _____
- Game night: _____
- Cook dinner together (something new): _____
- Attend sports event: _____
- Fly a kite together: _____
- Jet skiing: _____
- Jig-saw puzzle: _____
- Concert: _____
- Read a book together: _____
- Watch an old movie: _____
- Home project: _____

- Other: _____
- Other: _____
- Other: _____
- Other: _____
- Other: _____

Schedule It!

Everything you've done in this exercise so far is a complete, total, absolute, unmistakable, undeniable, indisputable, inescapable, 100 percent waste of time — unless you schedule the activities you checked! So take a few minutes to write down a date for several of these things you have checked above. Do this with your spouse. Schedule several activities over the next few weeks and months. You will especially need to schedule the big stuff, as you will need to set aside several days and financial resources for most of these. Try to do at least two or three "big" things in the next year, and one or two of the easier activities per month.

Dates for some big stuff for the next 12 months:

Activity: _____ Date: _____
Activity: _____ Date: _____
Activity: _____ Date: _____
Activity: _____ Date: _____
Activity: _____ Date: _____

Dates for easier experiences for the next three months:

Activity: _____ Date: _____
Activity: _____ Date: _____
Activity: _____ Date: _____
Activity: _____ Date: _____
Activity: _____ Date: _____
Activity: _____ Date: _____
Activity: _____ Date: _____
Activity: _____ Date: _____
Activity: _____ Date: _____

WEEK EIGHTEEN
Interaction with the Opposite Sex

According to the American Association for Marriage and Family Therapy, 25 percent of married men and 15 percent of married women have had extramarital affairs. Another 20 percent confess to "emotional affairs." Ruth Houston, founder of Infidelity/Advice.com, says one-third of marriages will be affected by an affair. These statistics focus only on physical sexual opposite-sex encounters, and do not include porn or masturbation activity.

Compounding the problem is the secrecy of inappropriate sexual behavior. In his book, *The Secrets of Surviving Infidelity*, Dr. Scott Haltzman writes, "Cheating men rarely tell their wives they cheated. Without being asked, just seven percent of men admitted to their wives that they cheated. Approximately 68 percent of men never admit to cheating or do so only after their wives have concrete evidence of the affairs."

The secrecy of porn and sex addiction creates a justifiable lack of trust for the wounded spouse. Why should she ever believe her husband when he says his late hours at work, lunch with his secretary, or texting with a female friend were completely innocent? Agreeing on what will be accepted as appropriate interaction with the opposite sex is one of the most challenging dilemmas for couples who have been rocked by infidelity.

Two extremes are either impossible or dangerous: (a) no interaction with the opposite sex, or (b) unbridled interaction with the opposite sex. So, the answer lies somewhere in between.

The Billy Graham Rule

Many husbands have adopted what has become known as the "Billy Graham Rule." In 1948, Billy Graham began a series of evangelistic meetings in Modesto, California, along with his ministry team of Cliff Barrows, George Beverly Shea, and Grady Wilson. The group met to discuss and adopt a series of policies which would hold them to the highest standards of biblical and moral integrity. Their agreement became known as the "Modesto Manifesto."

In his book, *Just As I Am*, Graham reflected on this agreement and what led to its adoption. "One afternoon, during the Modesto meetings, I called the team together to discuss the problem. Then I asked them to go to their rooms for an hour and list all the problems they could think of that evangelists and evangelism encountered. When they returned, the lists were remarkably similar."

One of the areas of concern was sexual integrity. They adopted the following policy as part of the Manifesto.

"We pledged among ourselves to avoid any situation that would have even the appearance of compromise or suspicion. From that day on, I did not travel, meet or eat alone with a woman other than my wife."

This was a policy which I (Mark) adopted and implemented for my staff and myself while serving as senior pastor to three churches. Though such a practice invites criticism from many from the outside, we find that this policy is well-suited for rebuilding trust and protecting both partners from unnecessary temptation and criticism.

David and Bathsheba
2 Samuel 11

The story of David and Bathsheba is well-documented and is rife with application for married men. We assume the reader is familiar with the story, and will only use this space to address the aspects from the story that address the topic before us. We see three principles from this biblical account that apply to the subject of interaction with the opposite sex. There are several reasons David got into trouble.

1. David had no accountability.

It is clear from this story that David answered only to himself. When he saw Bathsheba across the way, bathing, he didn't reach out to anyone for help. In fact, most of his men were off at war, where he was supposed to be. David was the king, the most powerful man in the land. He was accountable to no one.

2. David had set no boundaries.

There are several guardrails that David could have put in place. Don't talk to a woman with your wife not present. Don't let your eyes wander in inappropriate directions. When you see a beautiful woman, bounce your eyes. Don't leave your room or home when alone. Don't allow a woman into your home when your wife is away.

3. David was not prepared for disclosure.

The cover-up was worse than the crime. It was bad enough that the king had violated his marriage vows as he violated Bathsheba. Then he had a binary choice: either (a) come clean, or (b) cover up. He chose to cover up, which meant sending Bathsheba's husband to the front lines of war where he would be killed in order that David might take Bathsheba as his wife, thus making the pending birth of the child conceived from his sinful act explainable by virtue of his sudden marriage to Bathsheba.

Practical Guidelines

There are no universal one-size-fits-all guidelines for interaction with the opposite sex. The wounding of the addict's spouse, combined with the addict's history of unwise choices dictate that any interaction he has with the opposite sex must be carefully considered. It is best to err on the side of no interaction rather than too much interaction. We suggest the following guidelines for married couples who are recovering from the trauma of porn or sex addiction — especially when physical or emotional contact has been a part of the addict's past.

1. Agree on appropriate boundaries.

Some level of interaction between people of opposite sexes is going to be part of life, and male/female friendships outside of marriage are inevitable. But very clear boundaries must be put in place. These boundaries must be agreed upon in advance. And any boundary with which the wounded spouse is not comfortable is not a good boundary.

2. Include your spouse in the friendship.

There should be no friendships that both spouses are not aware of or that both spouses do not support. There will be instances in which the married man, for example, has necessary interaction with women at work, out of view from his wife. And circumstances may be such that the wife never meets the women from his work. But she must be aware of her and any interaction her husband has with them.

3. These friendships should not be close.

Any time spent with someone of the opposite sex should be limited and impersonal. Such topics as her marital struggles or emotional needs are off limits for discussion. Hugs and intimate discussions are off limits. The married man should never discuss anything with the opposite sex that he would not be comfortable saying if his wife was in the room.

4. Texting and social media contacts should be limited.

Any texting with the opposite sex should only be done with the spouse's consent and knowledge. There will be times when texts or social media posts are appropriate, depending on three 't's — the (a) topic, (b) timing, and (c) tenor of the message. A good practice is for the husband and wife to make their devices available for review by their spouse.

5. Opposite-sex friendships should be out in the open.

If a man has a series of conversations with a woman at work, church, or some other setting, he should be sure his wife is completely in the know on this. There should never be opposite-sex friendships on any level of which his wife is not aware.

6. Any opposite-sex friend needs to know you prioritize your marriage.

Include your wife/husband on text streams with the opposite sex. Praise your spouse to the opposite sex. Let your love for your spouse be clear. Display pictures of your family at work. Your friend or co-worker of the opposite sex should never doubt where your priorities lie.

7. Don't be alone with someone of the opposite sex.

As stated in the "Modesto Manifesto," none of us should be alone with someone other than our spouse — at lunch, in the car, or in our office. The rare exceptions are for therapists and other professionals whose work dictates professional settings in which a man and woman might be alone for brief periods of time. But these should be reduced, managed, and eliminated if necessary, to rebuild trust.

8. Conduct honest self-appraisal.

If you find yourself defending your time with the opposite sex, your texting with the opposite sex, or any other behavior which makes your spouse feel uncomfortable, take honest stock of your real motivations. It may be that the only person you are fooling is yourself.

Conclusion

Few things can derail a couple's recovery like continued contact with the opposite sex. It is imperative that you, as a couple, agree on what is acceptable for you. Keep in mind, as your trust in one another grows, these guidelines may evolve to a small degree. And always agree that when there is disagreement on these boundaries, it is the wounded spouse who holds the "trump card." She/he must feel safe again. And if that presents an inconvenience to the addicted spouse, that is an inconvenience he/she should welcome.

THIS WEEK'S EXERCISE
Setting Up Ground Rules

How much interaction is okay? How much is too much? What type of interaction is acceptable? There is a lot of gray area here. Each couple needs to decide the extent to which they are comfortable with their spouse interacting with other adults of the opposite sex. Of course, there are obvious lines we can all agree should never be crossed. For this exercise, it is important to address those areas that may not be so obvious. The litmus test is simple. You should agree to not cross any lines that make your husband or wife uncomfortable. And this may be a moving target. As you move further into recovery, it may be that your spouse becomes more comfortable with some forms of interaction with which she or he is not comfortable right now.

Below, we will lay out several ways in which we might interact with others of the opposite sex. Check the ones which you want your husband or wife to avoid, at least until further notice. Then share your lists with each other and try to reach an agreement on what is — and is not — in bounds.

Which do you find unacceptable?

_____ Meeting for lunch
_____ Private discussion of each other's marriage
_____ Driving in the car together
_____ Other personal discussions
_____ Private meetings that are work-related
_____ Private meetings that are not work-related
_____ Any texting that does not include your spouse on the thread
_____ Texting of a private matter
_____ Private phone calls
_____ Personal emails
_____ Private social media contacts
_____ Saving contact data without spouse's knowledge

What other lines do you want to make sure are not crossed?

- _____

- _____

- _____

- _____
- _____

WEEK NINETEEN
Fighting Fair

Marriage is the union of two imperfect people. What could go wrong? Some degree of conflict is inevitable. Toss sex or porn addiction into the mix and you have the recipe for disaster. But if the couple is committed to recovery — for the addict, the spouse, and the marriage — God will step in. A commitment to the marriage does not mean there will be no more conflict. We can guarantee conflict will come. The issue is how you deal with it.

One guy asked his wife, "Why did God make you so beautiful, yet so dumb?" His wife answered, "God made me beautiful so you would love me. He made me dumb so I would love you."

Since the days of Adam and Eve, beautiful, dumb people have been getting married. And conflict has ensued. So the question is not *whether* you will fight, but *how* you will fight. We suggest you fight fair, and we will try to show you what that looks like.

Potiphar and His Wife
Genesis 39

Although one of the clearest accounts of how a man should reject sexual temptation is that of Joseph and Potiphar's wife, the backstory is also interesting. Why did Mrs. Potiphar pursue Joseph so relentlessly? What was going on in her marriage this whole time? Let's consider their story, then we will identify five egregious mistakes that emanated from this couple's inability to communicate and "fight fair."

Potiphar was a high ranking official in Egypt, where Joseph had been sold by the Ishmaelites. As Joseph found favor of God and man, he quickly moved up the ranks of service under Potiphar's command, to a position of overseer of his property, which included his house.

Potiphar's wife soon "took notice of Joseph and said, 'Come to bed with me!'" (Genesis 39:7).

Joseph refused her advances, but she persisted "day after day" (39:10).

Then, one day when none of the other servants was present, Mrs. Potiphar became more aggressive. When he ran out of the house, she grabbed his coat and called for the household servants, accusing Joseph of attempted sexual assault (39:13-15).

When Potiphar returned home his wife stuck to her story, and he had Joseph put in jail. With God's continued favor, Joseph again rose through the ranks and was put in a place of authority in prison, and enjoyed the approval of the warden (39:21-23).

Now, let's identify six examples of how Mrs. Potiphar grossly mishandled the situation.

Mistake #1 — Poor boundaries

Mrs. Potiphar was in the house with Joseph, knowing no one else was there. Joseph's work required that he be there. And let's not put this all on Mrs. Potiphar; her husband is at fault for allowing a situation in which neither he nor his servants would be at the house.

Mistake #2 — Playing with fire

The first time Potiphar's wife was turned away by Joseph should have been a clear warning to her. She should have learned from her near-fall and avoided tempting situations going forward. Instead, she played with fire, talking to Joseph every day. Continued secretive contact with someone of the opposite sex is dangerous.

Mistake #3 — Sin and betrayal

Mrs. Potiphar failed in her attempt to seduce Joseph. But his refusal to go to bed with her did not exonerate her intents. She was as guilty as if he had agreed to her scheme every day. She sinned against God and betrayed the vows of her marriage.

Mistake #4 — Triangulation

Joseph's seducer immediately brought the other servants into the situation. She tried to use them against Joseph, knowing that her position as Potiphar's wife would influence the other servants to side with her against this Israelite. It's called triangulation. It's what spouses often do to shift the blame from their own bad choices.

Mistake #5 — Gaslighting

Mrs. Potiphar turned the blame onto her husband: "That Hebrew slave you brought us came to me to make sport of me" (39:17). She blamed her husband for the situation she was in, rather than own her actions of betrayal.

Mistake #6 — Anger

Now we see Potiphar's response. "He burned with anger" (39:19). Rather than get the facts or own his part (he never should have allowed for this set-up in the first place), he reacted with emotion and anger. There was no discussion between Potiphar and his wife; they did just about everything wrong that could be done wrong in this series of events.

How to Fight Fair

Joseph Joubert said, "The aim of argument, or of discussion, should not be victory, but progress." The "fight" between a husband and wife should not be the dragging of one party over to the other side as the objective. Rather, they should aim for understanding and progress. Will Rogers was right when he said, "People's minds are rarely changed through argument."

So how do we "fight fair"? We offer several principles.

1. Both parties should come out ahead.

In order for one party to win the argument, both parties must win the argument. Dr. Grant Brenner says it like this: "For a fight to be fair, all participants must come out ahead. If a fight is destructive, it is unfair to all because it brings everyone down."

Couples must think "both/and" rather than "either/or." Many times, the husband is more naturally wired to debate, utilizing data points, while the wife is more concerned with sharing her heart and expressing her pain. They need to come together with a common goal of both parties coming out ahead.

2. Offer to make the first move.

If you want to see reconciliation and reach closure, move in that direction yourself. Be the one to change first. The effort you make to change the tone of an increasingly nasty exchange can, over time, save and strengthen the marriage.

Dr. Harriet Lerner addressed this in her book, *Why Won't You Apologize: Healing Big Betrayals and Everyday Hurts*. She writes, "Overcoming the LDD (Listening Deficit Disorder) is the essential ingredient of the heartfelt apology — the best tool we have to mend fences and heal broken connections." Make the first move.

3. Avoid hyperbole.

Don't say things like, "You always do that" or "You never do this." Words like "always" and "never" only pour gas on the fire. In their article, *Fighting Fair*, Rob Pascale and Lou Primavera write, "Nobody does all things right or wrong. When confronted with 'always,' partners are required to point out the occasions when they did not do or say what is claimed. This leads to escalation."

4. Pick your timing.

The timing of the "fight" often matters as much as the substance. Don't try to resolve conflict in times of stress or exhaustion. Any difficult discussion that begins at the wrong time will usually lead to a toxic encounter that is anything but productive.

Michelle Farris is a marriage and family therapist who specializes in codependency and anger management. She counsels couples, "Timing plays a big role in managing conflict. So before initiating a potentially difficult chat, check in with yourself. When you're not feeling great emotionally or physically it's easier to react impulsively and regret it later."

THIS WEEK'S EXERCISE
Set Up Some Ground Rules

For this week's exercise, you will do three things. First, you will make a list of things you commit to doing in order to fight fair. Second, you will make a list of expectations for your spouse — those things you want from him or her, as ground rules for your next "heated fellowship." Third, you will share these lists with your husband or wife.

Part A — Your Personal Commitment

Write down a few things you promise to do (or not do) during any future disagreements or arguments with your spouse:

- _____
- _____
- _____
- _____
- _____

Part B — Your Expectations

Write down a few expectations you want your partner to agree to, concerning his or her behavior when you "fight":

- _____
- _____

- _____
- _____
- _____

Part C — Share Your Lists

As a couple, write down up to five things you agree upon, as ground rules for when you have spirited fellowship times in the future:

- _____
- _____
- _____
- _____
- _____

compartmentalize his lifestyle and continue his destructive behaviors with as little inner strife as possible. Of course, this is a house of cards, which will inevitably come crashing down. But until he is desperate to get well, his denial will lead to one thing.

Gaslighting.

As we have seen in this week's reading, gaslighting is a learned skill, honed by many years of practice. The result of efficient gaslighting is that (a) the addict continues his downward spiral, and (b) his wife comes to see herself as the problem, crazy, and detached from reality.

Your participation in the couples' recovery group indicates a high probability that you have begun to come down on the other side of the gaslighting mountain. Let's facilitate that process.

Part A — Express your story.

Write out a few ways in which you think you have been a gas lighter before your partner. If you are the wounded spouse, use this space to describe the gaslighting you have been subjected to by your spouse.

_____
_____
_____
_____
_____
_____
_____
_____
_____
_____
_____

Part B — Role play

This is for the wounded spouse. Take a few minutes and play the role of your husband gaslighting. Make it as true to form as possible. No embellishing! After you have taken a few minutes to demonstrate an example of gaslighting by your spouse, share your feelings with one another.

Part C — Never again!

Now talk to your husband or wife about ways you will seek to end all gaslighting as a couple.

WEEK TWENTY-ONE
Serving Each Other

Saint John Chrysostom said, "The love of husband and wife is the force that welds society together." Nothing threatens that bond more than sexual betrayal. And nothing overcomes that betrayal quite like both husband and wife committing to a lifetime of serving one another. We all long to have the kind of marriage Martin Luther described: "Let the wife make the husband glad to come home, and let him make her sorry to see him leave." Serving one another is a huge step in that direction.

This week, we will get really practical, with specific tips on how to serve your spouse. Let's begin with a quick look at the ultimate example from Scripture.

The Ultimate Example
1 Corinthians 13

Though this passage was not written specifically to married couples, it still works! The Apostle Paul essentially defines true love (agape love) as what we do, not what we feel. And this is exactly what service is all about. Let's pull out a few examples of how love correlates to service within a marriage.

1. Service is more than words.

Paul begins by saying that empty speech is as a "clanging cymbal" (1 Corinthians 13:1). He says that even the most gifted communicator cannot let his words become a substitute for actions. I (Beth) tell clients often, "Believe their behaviors, not their words."

2. Service is more than spiritual activity.

Paul says that "faith that can move mountains" is incomplete (13:2). Many times, a husband will substitute God talk for real action. It's called "spiritual masking," and many of us are really good at it. A strong spiritual connection with God is not genuine until it expresses itself in service to others.

3. Service requires patience.

Paul enumerates the characteristics of true love beginning in verse four. And of all the traits of agape love, it is patience that rises to the top of his list. He begins, "Love is patient" (13:4). For the couple infected with the disease of addiction, this means that both parties must give the other person the necessary space to process their trauma and find secure footing, emotionally, physically, and spiritually.

4. Service is a daily routine.

Serving one's spouse is not a matter of planning a huge anniversary dinner or going on a fun outing. Although those can be major marriage builders, it is the day-to-day way we treat each other that makes the real difference. Paul suggests several ways this works: (a) kindness toward one another, (b) humility, (c) making selfless decisions, (d) controlling our tempers, (e) forgiveness, and (f) mutual support.

5. Service always does four things.

Paul then turns to four things love always does. Catch the word "always." In his own words, "Love always protects, always trusts, always hopes, always perseveres" (13:7). These four trademarks are constants in real love and genuine service from one spouse toward the other.

General Service by Both Spouses

There are several ways we can serve each other in marriage. Writing for *In Touch*, Kim Gosselin offered five suggestions.

1. Do something simple.

Don't make service too complicated. Sometimes, simple is better.
Examples: leave love notes, unload the dishwasher, help with the children, fill the car up with gas, wash the car, bring your spouse a snack, give up the remote for one hour

2. Unplug.

Gosselin writes, "Our technology-rich lives are full of distractions. Smartphones, TVs, and computers all compete to steal our focus. Paying attention to your spouse is one great way to serve them. Set aside time each day to unplug from technology and focus on your mate."

Examples: no smart phones after dinner, no emails on weekends, no texting during dinner

3. Prioritize intimacy.

Husbands and wives serve one another by cultivating a thriving sexual relationship in which they seek to meet one another's needs.

Examples: date nights, fresh outings, recovery nights

4. Sacrifice.

Paul said, "Through love, serve one another" (Galatians 5:13). This involves doing things we might not enjoy ourselves, in order to please our mates.

Examples: entering into your spouse's hobbies, cooking his/her favorite meal, hanging out with his/her friends

5. Serve spiritually.

Don't leave out the God-component. It is easy for us to serve God individually, but we serve each other best when we serve God together.

Examples: serving in church together, praying together at night, helping other couples in recovery

How a Husband Can Serve His Wife

It is interesting to note that while husbands are commanded to love their wives (Ephesians 5:25), Scripture never puts this demand on women. The bar is high for the husband's expression of love. "Husbands, love your wives, just as Christ loved the church and gave himself up for her" (5:25). The purpose of his love, the Bible says, is that his wife might become more like God (5:26-27).

Now, let's get specific. Here are some very practical ways in which a husband can love/serve his wife.

1. Take your wife on a weekly date night.
2. Call or text your wife during your work day.
3. Help out around the house.
4. Be attentive to her conversation.
5. Surprise her with occasional notes, cards, or flowers.
6. Set aside time to pray with her.
7. Lead your children spiritually.
8. Have your family active in a local church.
9. Listen to her fears.
10. Guard your eyes in public.
11. Avoid correcting your wife in public.
12. Open the car door.

How a Wife Can Serve Her Husband

While the husband is called to love his wife, the wife is called to esteem her husband. The idea of "submission" (Ephesians 5) means to "put him on a pedestal." The husband needs to feel important. It's a guy thing. They want to be the hero, the fixer, the one whose presence is indispensable. Here are a few ways to serve your husband.

1. Cook his favorite meal.
2. Engage his interests and hobbies.
3. Encourage his "man cave" time.
4. Celebrate his recovery.
5. Leave him love notes.
6. Pray for him daily.
7. Brag on him — in public.
8. Give him the benefit of the doubt.
9. Thank him for providing financially.
10. Rub his back or shoulders.
11. Surprise him with small gifts.
12. Ask about his work.

Conclusion

Zig Ziglar said, "Many marriages would be better if the husband and the wife clearly understood that they are on the same side." One of the best ways to get "on the same side" is through mutual service. My (Mark's) old pastor, Dr. Cecil Sewell, often said, "You can give without loving, but you can't love without giving." That starts at home, in the wonderful relationship we call marriage.

THIS WEEK'S EXERCISE
Toss Mind-Reading to the Curb

Christian comedian Ken Davis says women play this game called "I've got a problem and I'm not going to tell you [my husband] what it is, but you better figure it out on your own if you don't want to wake up in the freezer in the garage that nobody knows about."

Women are the more intuitive of the human species. They naturally assume their husband is a whole lot brighter than he really is. The fact is, we (men) are not mind readers. Ladies, if there's something you want us to know — SAY IT!

Dr. Gary Chapman lists "acts of service" as one of the five love languages. Whether this is your love language or not, you would be so much happier if you husband or wife was a bit more intentional about serving you.

So let's do it!

Small Act of Service

Come up with one thing you will do to bless your spouse this week. Make it something that doesn't cost much time or money. And put it on your calendar. If you plan the act, but don't schedule it, we're pretty sure it won't happen. Then check it off once you've completed this act of service.

- Your small act of service: _____
- Date to complete the act: _____
- You did it: _____

Big Act of Service

Now think a little bigger. What is something a little more demanding that you can do for your husband or wife?

1. Your bigger act of service: _____
2. Date to complete it: _____
3. You did it: _____

WEEK TWENTY-TWO
Expectations

Alexander Pope said, "Blessed is he who expects nothing, for he shall never be disappointed." Pope may be onto something. Unrealistic expectations can be a damaging force for any couple — especially one who is recovering from the ravages of sexual addiction and betrayal.

Experts seem to agree that the expectations bar only gets higher with time. Relationship therapist Esther Perel tells us that expectations have risen worldwide and that they are particularly high in the United States. And Eli Finkel, a psychology professor at Northwestern University, says that expectations within marriage have increased over the past few decades, while the time people actually invest in their marriages has decreased. He says that these changes have correlated with all-time levels of dissatisfaction with being married.

So let's talk about it. We will start by addressing unreasonable expectations within a marriage. Then we will pivot to the obvious — reasonable expectations among married couples. We will save this week's biblical account for last. We will offer five ways to regulate your expectations from a familiar — but unlikely — story from the New Testament.

Unreasonable Expectations

There is a phrase borrowed from AA that all couples in recovery would do well to apply: "It's about progress, not perfection." The fact is, apart from his addiction, your husband had issues anyway. (And so do you.) Step 4 calls them "character flaws." We all have them. And while you should expect your recovering spouse — husband or wife — to make progress in all areas of life, it is important to tamp down your expectations to a reasonable level.

We like the way Donald Miller put it: "When you stop expecting people to be perfect, you can like them for who they are."

Years ago, the couples on our church staff played a form of *The Newlywed Game*. One of the questions was, "What will your husband say is his most annoying habit?" To everyone's shock and dismay, one wife said, "Larry (not his real name) doesn't have any annoying habits." Worse yet, she got the answer right. That is exactly what Larry predicted that his wife would say.

The rest of the church staff immediately offered to name Larry's annoying habits — by the dozen!

We all have annoying habits. And none of us will ever be Jesus. The sooner you recognize that some of the expectations you have put on your spouse may never come to fruition, the happier you will be.

Here are a few examples of unrealistic expectations within marriage:

- Your spouse should fulfill your every need.
- Your spouse should serve as the primary source of your happiness.
- Your spouse should fill all of your companionship needs — and you should fill all of hers/his.
- Your spouse should mirror what is important to you.
- You should always be the center of attention for your spouse.
- The excitement and passion should continue as it was earlier in your relationship.

Reasonable Expectations

The fact that many of your expectations of your spouse are *unreasonable* doesn't mean there are no expectations that are *reasonable*. It is the process of agreeing on what those reasonable expectations are that brings life to the relationship.

Dr. Dianne Grande, licensed clinical psychologist, wrote an article in 2018, titled, "How Expectations Affect One's Happiness in Marriage." She concluded, "The happiest couples tailor their expectations to what is realistic for their own circumstances. They follow basic guidelines of kindness, respect, and trust that the other person has their back."

Tonda Bian wrote an interesting article titled, "12 Reasonable Expectations that Could Save Your Marriage." These expectations follow:

- Commitment to the marriage
- Verbal affection
- Compassion and empathy for each other's feelings
- Respect for each other
- Consideration for each other's differences
- Spending quality time with each other
- Showing interest in each other and what each is involved with
- Physical closeness: hugging, holding hands, touching
- Generosity of thought, spirit, and action toward one another
- Acknowledging that there are other important people in each spouse's life

- Making time and creating opportunities to have fun and laughter together
- Open communication and sincere listening to one another

How to Regulate Our Expectations
The Prodigal Son and His Dad
Luke 15

We are all familiar with the story of the prodigal son. Jesus tells this lengthy parable in Luke 15 as a part of a triad — the lost son, the lost sheep, and the lost coin. As the story goes, a son went to his father and asked for his inheritance before his father's death. Dad agreed, and off the boy went — to a far-away land where he wasted his resources and slipped deeper and deeper into a life of debauchery in his search for purpose and meaning.

Eventually, the boy came to his senses. After he came to his senses, he came to his father. Dad was happy to receive his boy back, and a grand party was thrown in his honor. All were happy, except for the son's brother, who moped in a pool of self-pity. But we'll save that part of the story for another day.

What we have here is a father who would have never imagined that his son would leave home — and all of the values Dad had taught him through the years. So Dad had a decision to make. How would he handle this? Specifically, how would he regulate his expectations of his son? We see five principles here.

1. Dad understood his son's brokenness.

The father gave his son the money, and did not try to control how he would spend it (Luke 15:12-13). What Dad knew about his son, each of us needs to understand about our spouse. We are all broken — not just the sex addict. When we recognize the broken nature of our mate, we can regulate our expectations much easier. In theological terms, people aren't sinners because they sin as much as they sin because they're sinners.

2. Dad gave his son room to fail.

The good father did not stand in his son's way. He knew that any effort to do so would only delay the inevitable. So Dad let the boy go (15:13). If it had been my son, sensing the massive mistakes he was about to fall into, my instinct would have been to protect him against himself. That would mean seizing control in any way I could. But the fact is, we cannot control our adult children. And you cannot control your spouse. Yes, the addict should probably be on Covenant Eyes. Yes, you should limit the amount of cash he carries. Yes, guardrails should be put in place. But never dismiss the possibility that he has the opportunity to drive off the cliff anyway. You must give him room to fail.

3. Dad didn't chase after his son.

Even when a major famine struck the land, the father didn't chase after his son (15:14). When a spouse strays, sometimes the best (and hardest) thing the spouse can do is to let them go. This wealthy father could have easily gone after his son, and likely found him. But he had the wisdom to understand that his son needed to come back home because of what was happening in him, not to him. So Dad waited, for what must have seemed like an eternity. Sometimes that is all we can do.

4. Dad listened to his behaviors.

We love this part of the story. If you read the account carefully, you will find that the wayward son — once he decided that he would return — comprised a very detailed speech which he would deliver to his father. You can read it for yourself (15:18-19). Then, when the boy came back to his father, he launched into this speech. But Dad cut him off early in his prepared remarks (15:21). What the boy began to say in verse 21 was exactly what he had planned to say in verses 18-19. That's how we know the words were memorized. He had probably played this out in his head dozens of times on the road back home.

But then Dad did the unexpected. In his excitement to welcome his boy back home, he just jumped in, and the celebration began. Did the father not need to know of his son's repentance? Of course, he needed to know that. But Dad was wise enough to listen to his son's behavior, rather than his words.

We must do the same thing in marriage, especially when rocked by betrayal. When an addict presents a Disclosure to his wife, he often sees that as a finish line, the end to a long and difficult process. But the wife sees it as the starting line, the beginning of a new opportunity. But she will be listening to his behaviors far more than his words.

5. Dad celebrated his son's change.

Dad didn't question his son's sincerity or whether his change would last (15:22-24). Rather, he chose to celebrate what he knew. Never let the uncertainty of the future rob you of the blessings of the moment. None of us can be certain that our mate will remain faithful for life. But what we can do is celebrate the positive change that has already taken place.

For some couples, sobriety anniversaries are times of great celebration. Other couples are triggered by these dates. So you will need to find your own sweet spot here. But however you celebrate progress, do it enthusiastically.

Conclusion

We want to leave you with one more thought on the expectation game. There are two ways this can work.

Way #1 — For most of us, we wait on our spouse to hit it out of the park, and then we raise our expectations in response.

Way #2 — A few of us have discovered that if we raise our expectations of our spouse, he will often rise to that level. As leadership expert Stephen Covey wrote, "Treat a man as he is and he will remain as he is. Treat a man as he can and should be and he will become as he can and should be."

We embrace Way #2. Within reason, let your spouse know that you expect the best, hope for the best, and are praying for the best. Then get ready, because your expectations just might be met.

THIS WEEK'S EXERCISE
Great Expectations

Sylvia Plath wrote, "If you expect nothing from anybody, you're never disappointed." While that may be true, in marriage, you deserve much more than that. You have every right to expect certain things from your husband or wife. Even if you are the addicted spouse, and you have crushed your spouse's heart, it is healthy to have certain expectations of him or her.

Depending on where you each are in your own recovery, your expectations will vary. Take your time and write these from your heart. Then, after you have made a list of expectations for your spouse, prepare these lists with each other. List up to ten expectations you have for your spouse.

1. _____

2. _____

3. _____

4. _____

5. _____

6. _____

7. _____

8. _____

9. _____

10. _____

WEEK TWENTY-THREE
Playtime

Never underestimate the value of having fun. The old axiom is true — the family that prays together stays together. But it is also true that the family that plays together stays together. This has been a hallmark of our marriage and of our family from the beginning. We are each other's best friends. We have fun together. We have discovered the value of play. In fact, playtime is one of God's gifts that helped us through the deepest valleys.

Research supports this. "Having fun together can help couples feel positive emotions, which can increase relationship satisfaction, help couples to unite in order to overcome differences, and give hope when working through difficult challenges" (Aune & Wong, 2002).

More importantly, Scripture supports the value of playtime. Consider two passages from the Old Testament.

"The streets of the city shall be full of boys and girls playing in its streets" (Zechariah 8:5).

"You shall eat before the Lord your God, and you shall rejoice, you and your households, in all that you undertake, in which the Lord your God has blessed you" (Deuteronomy 12:7).

Solomon is remembered primarily for two things: wisdom and wealth. But he was also a bit of a marriage expert. Consider the following passages from the Book of Ecclesiastes. Remember, as you read these, that Ecclesiastes was a bit of a downer. If you are a melancholy, you get Ecclesiastes. If you aren't a melancholy, you avoid Ecclesiastes. But for all its solemnness, the book offers several insights to the importance of having a good time within the marriage relationship.

Solomon and His Wife (Wives)
Ecclesiastes

We will let these passages stand on their own. Read them slowly, asking yourself if this kind of play/fun is descriptive of your marriage.

"There is nothing better for a person than that he should eat and drink and find enjoyment in his toil. This also, I saw, is from the hand of God" (Ecclesiastes 2:24).

"I commend joy, for man has no good thing under the sun but to eat and drink and be joyful, for this will go with him in his toil through the days of his life that God has given him under the sun" (Ecclesiastes 8:15).

"For everything there is a season, and a time for every matter under heaven . . . a time to weep and a time to laugh" (Ecclesiastes 3:1, 5).

"Rejoice, young man, in your youth, and let your heart cheer you in the days of your youth" (Ecclesiastes 11:9).

A bonus verse from Proverbs, also written by King Solomon: "A joyful heart is good medicine, but a crushed spirit dries up the bones" (Proverbs 17:22).

The Purpose of Play

Someone has said, "Getting married is like trading the adoration of many for the sarcasm of one." A little sarcasm can be a good thing. For us, it works!

Whether you incorporate sarcasm into your playtime routine or not, embrace playtime as a part of your growth as a couple. As Diane Ackerman said, "Play is our brain's favorite way of learning."

For the rest of this chapter we will borrow heavily from the thoughts of Dr. Naomi Brewer, of Utah State University. She has written a marvelous piece on her university's website, titled, "Have Fun! The Importance of Play in Couple Relationships." She writes, "When couples first meet, they usually spend a significant amount of time engaging in fun activities together and spending quality time getting to know each other. They plan to keep the fun and spark in their relationship, but it eventually takes a back seat to other priorities."

The purpose of play, Brewer says, is to "increase bonding, communication, conflict resolution, and relationship satisfaction."

Defining Play

What, exactly, is playtime? We define play as "any pleasurable use of discretionary time." Mark Twain said it like this: "Work consists of whatever a body is obliged to do. Play consists of whatever a body is not obliged to do."

Play is a gift of God. It is meant to be embraced, celebrated, and utilized. You don't need to make time for work; that seems to take care of itself. But you do need to carve out time for play, especially in marriage.

What is the value of play? Plato said, "You can discover more about a person in an hour of play than in a year of conversation."

We agree.

Overcoming Barriers to Playtime

When a couple has been traumatized by the ravages of sex addiction, playtime is the last thing on the docket. Life becomes a matter of simple survival, from one moment to the next. Playing a game of croquet in the backyard is usually not the first thing a couple thinks about following a Disclosure.

We suggest taking the following steps to overcome the natural barriers to playtime. These are adopted from Dr. Naomi Brewer, cited earlier in the chapter.

1. Schedule fun times.
2. Get active.
3. Give yourself permission to be a kid again.
4. Try new things.
5. Protect fun from conflict and resentment.
6. Focus on teamwork.
7. Budget for some fun.
8. Make having fun more of a priority.

Keeping the Fun Alive

If you want to feel good about your marriage, visit any IHOP on a Saturday morning. You will find booths filled with couples who have been married for 40 or 50 years. If you watch carefully, you will observe that for most, engaging conversation has long been replaced with reading the newspaper and working crossword puzzles at the restaurant.

Many couples are like the children of God in the wilderness. They really didn't have 40 years of experience. What they really had was one year, 40 times. If your Bible has maps in the back, look it up. They just kept going in circles for 40 years.

The challenge for any couple is to keep the fun alive, to quit going in circles. As we get older, we tend to play less.

George Bernard Shaw wrote, "We don't stop playing because we grow old; we grow old because we stop playing."

Dr. Brewer weighs in: "Strong, healthy, happy, and long-lasting relationships do not just happen. They require effort. And one of the things every relationship needs is a little fun. Be intentional about having fun in your relationship. As you become aware of the barriers to fun and take action to overcome them, you will find greater happiness in your marriage and in life in general."

(b) identify any negative or triggering dates, and (c) share these dates with your mate, so you will know how to recognize these dates (or not) in the future.

Part A — Write down any dates that are cause for celebration, and state why.

- _____

- _____

- _____

- _____

- _____

Part B — Write down any dates that are triggering or painful and state why.

- _____

- _____

- _____

- _____

- _____

Meet with your spouse and exchange your responses.

WEEK TWENTY-FIVE
Reflective Listening

O ne man was asked why he had not spoken to his wife in 25 years. "I was taught that it is rude to interrupt," he said. There was another couple who struggled with good listening skills. In the heat of the discussion, the wife said, "I'm sorry . . . did the middle of my sentence interrupt the beginning of yours?"

Good listening is a skill learned by too few couples. It is especially important on the heel of the discovery of a sexual addiction.

Solomon, who was the marriage expert of his day, recorded a passage from the Book of Proverbs which speaks to the subject of listening.

Solomon's Advice on Listening

Proverbs 25:11-15 "A word fitly spoken is like apples of gold in a setting of silver. Like a gold ring or an ornament of gold is a wise reprover to a listening ear. Like the cold of snow in the time of harvest is a faithful messenger to those who send him; he refreshes the soul of his masters. Like clouds and wind without rain is a man who boasts of a gift he does not give. With patience a ruler may be persuaded, and a soft tongue will break a bone."

What Solomon Is Saying

Let's break down the message of King Solomon, and apply it to the modern couple. As we go verse-by-verse through this passage, we pull out several distinct principles that apply perfectly to the marital relationship.

Verse 11

These "words fitly spoken" come from a pure heart. Apples are fruit much desired and gold symbolizes the purity of God. We see here, the fruit of these lips come from a heart filled with the purity of God. These "pictures of silver" are beautiful in symbolism as well. Silver symbolizes redemption. When we see a person who speaks godly words, we know that they have been redeemed.

Verse 12

The ring is an earring, attached to the body. This "ornament of fine gold" means that this message is one of beauty and redemption. The husband who speaks to his wife this way is providing wisdom, comfort, and peace.

Verse 13

What we have in this verse is a refreshing coolness which helps in the time of harvest. A heavy snow would bring disaster, but this is just a cooling off and moment of refreshment. A faithful messenger is refreshing to his partner.

Verse 14

Clouds and wind ordinarily bring rain. To expect rain and not have it come was disappointing, especially to the people of these times. Similarly, a spouse who promises to communicate well with his wife, but fails to do so, is a disappointment.

Verse 15

This is a person who remains calm and speaks without anger. A king will listen and be persuaded. Soft words have more influence than force. You can break a person's bones and still not convince him, but a soft word is easy to listen to and will be more acceptable.

Five Ways to Be a Good Listener

Every couple at least says they want to learn better communication skills. Every spouse says he or she wants to become a better listener. We are here to help. We lean on the counsel of Drs. Les and Leslie Parrott, who have decades of training and expertise in this field. We pass along these five tips from them.

1. Listen with empathy.

When you practice empathy, you are putting yourself in your spouse's position and seeing things through their eyes. The Parrotts write, "Whether you're trying to resolve a conflict or just simply listening to your spouse talk about their day, it's beneficial to both of you to listen with empathy when your spouse speaks to you."

2. Listen for emotion.

When your spouse needs to talk to you about something — especially if it's something hard for them to talk about — it is easy to get wrapped up and carried away by your own emotions on the topic. In that case, you might respond to your spouse in a totally inappropriate way in your attempt to alleviate the difficult emotions that come up for you. Instead, take a minute to listen for what your spouse might be feeling. This type of intentional listening goes hand-in-hand with empathy.

3. Listen without bias.

Both you and your spouse have your own opinions, and it's hard to let those opinions go in favor of simply listening to one another. Listening without bias is helpful when you have opposite stances on certain issues, or when you're locked in a stalemate during a fight. Set your opinions aside long enough to hear what your spouse is saying, then practice your empathy skills to try to understand why.

4. Listen lovingly.

Les Parrott writes, "When you're communicating with your spouse, it can be helpful to use loving gestures and body language to let them know you care about what they have to say." It can be as simple as holding eye contact and nodding to affirm what they are telling you. You could also reach out to touch them or hold hands. Turn your body toward them as you talk.

5. Listen generously.

Your spouse needs the gift of your time and attention. It's hard to take time out of our busy lives to generously give our energy to listening when we have so much to do every day, but communicating openly is key to a healthy marriage. When you listen generously, your spouse will feel secure in coming to you with their concerns, hopes, and fears.

THIS WEEK'S EXERCISE
Listen Up!

Reflective listening requires the willingness to put personal perceptions, thoughts, and feelings aside in an attempt to understand those of someone else. This helps individuals to feel heard and validated. Agreement is not necessary.

So let's get started. Set aside a few minutes with your spouse for this exercise. During this time, you will each share an issue or problem, while the other listens. Then you will switch roles. Finally, you will each assess the experience.

One spouse speaks.

Share a problem or issue with which you currently struggle.

The other spouse listens.

It is important that you listen intently. Use nonverbal connectors such as eye contact, leaning forward toward your partner, nodding, and using appropriate facial expressions. Ask clarifying questions. Do not offer your opinion or suggestions. Restate what has been shared by way of summary. Include the emotions that were communicated, as well.

Example: "I can see that you felt left out when your coworkers went to lunch and did not invite you. That must have been hurtful." (It does not matter that your spouse may usually work through lunch, is regularly dieting, just had dental surgery, or eats like a slob!) Reflective listening is simply trying to connect with how the other person is feeling so he or she feels heard.

Switch roles.

Now, reverse roles. Repeat the exercise above.

Reflect on this exercise. Answer the following questions, and prepare to share your responses with your spouse.

- Did you feel heard? _____
- What did the listener do well? _____

  _____

- What could they have done better? _____

  _____

WEEK TWENTY-SIX

Self-Worth

Few challenges to a person's self-worth rival those brought on by sexual addiction. The addict loses his sense of self-worth when he says, "I must be a zero or I wouldn't have this struggle." His wife demonstrates a poor view of herself when she says, "I must not be worth much, or my husband wouldn't have gone outside our marriage in order to find sex."

What we want you to learn this week is that a healthy sense of self-worth is not a *condition* as much as it is a *choice*. That great scholar Michael J. Fox said it like this: "One's dignity may be assaulted, vandalized, and cruelly mocked, but it can never be taken away unless it is surrendered."

We also want you to recognize that your self-worth should never be tied to your spouse. Sure, that's easier said than done, but it is absolutely critical to your healing. Since your self-worth is not dependent on your spouse or his/her recovery, where does it come from?

God.

Let's dig deeper.

The Foundation of Self-Worth
Psalm 139:13-14

Psalms 139:13-14 "For you created my inmost being; you knit me together in my mother's womb. I praise you because I am fearfully and wonderfully made; your works are wonderful. I know that full well."

We see three overarching truths in these verses. It's not long and it is certainly not complicated.

1. God created your parts.

Did you catch that? The psalmist wrote, "You knit me together in my mother's womb." The Hebrew word for "knit" means to create very meticulously. When my grandmother knitted a blanket, she gave attention to every part. That's how God knitted you together.

Enough already with, "Well, I guess I'm loveable despite my big nose." No, you are loveable *because* of your big nose! Often the wife of a sex addict laments that if a certain body part looked "better," she would be more worthy of her husband's affection. I (Mark) get it. I have plenty of questions for God someday, about the way I was created. I'll start with my bunions, and go up from there. But the fact is, God created *your parts*, not *just you*.

2. The value is in the maker.

Why is a strand of Abe Lincoln's hair worth $10,000 on eBay? (And no, it's not real!) It's not because there is a hair shortage. I used to collect sports autographed memorabilia. A baseball signed by Babe Ruth is $10,000 more valuable than one not signed by Babe Ruth. It's not that Ruth's autograph turns the ball into a better ball, but that the buyer knows this ball was actually in the hand of Babe Ruth.

You are valuable because of your Maker. The mere fact that it is God who knit you together is all you need to know. The value is in the manufacturer, not the product.

3. Your creation makes God worthy of more praise.

Imagine that. The psalmist says that God is actually worthy of praise because he created the psalmist. It's not as if God was lacking in credentials worthy of praise. But when he made you, he got better! The fact that God created you the way he did is worthy of more praise to be heaped upon him. You can't be that bad, if your creation actually makes God look better!

Things That Don't Determine Your Self-Worth
We look for self-worth in all the wrong places. Here is a brief list of some of the ways many of us measure our self-worth, which always fall short.

- Your personal appearance
- Your job
- Your social media following
- Your age
- The opinions of others
- Your athleticism
- Your grades
- The number of friends you have
- Your relationship status
- How much money you have in the bank
- The place you live
- The car you drive
- The person you married

Signs of Strong Self-Esteem

So what are the signs of a strong sense of self-worth? These are just a few of those signs. You can create your own list, depending on your background and the nature of your struggles.

- You aren't afraid of feedback.
- You do not seek to please others or seek their approval.
- You are not afraid of conflict.
- You are able to set boundaries.
- You voice your needs and opinions.
- You are not a slave to perfection.
- You are not afraid of setbacks.
- You do not fear failure.
- You do not feel inferior.
- You accept who you are.

What People with Strong Self-Worth Say

We found this piece helpful. Michael Stanwyck is the co-founder of The Whole Life Challenge. Stanwyck is a successful mentor and coach. From working with thousands of clients, he has concluded that people with strong self-worth consistently say the following ten things about themselves.

1. "No matter what I've done, I'm worthy of love."

A person with a high sense of self-worth takes responsibility for his mistakes, but he does not degrade himself because of them.

2. "My things do not define me."

You are not the clothes you wear, the car you drive, or the relationship you do or do not have. Yes, it is healthy and fun to enjoy the finer things in life, but the person who honors their worthiness knows that they can enjoy external things without attaching identity to these things.

3. "I am allowed to feel the way I feel."

All feelings are legitimate. A person with strong self-worth creates space for their emotions without feeling guilty about them. They understand emotions are just tools that are helping them to pay attention.

4. "I delight in the joy of missing out."

A person of self-worth is not afraid to be alone. They love hanging out with their closest friends and family, but they also cherish alone time. This person doesn't go to parties and events simply because they are afraid to be left out. They believe that people who really matter will always welcome them, and even if they don't, they will still be okay.

5. "Life is about my response."

Those with a healthy sense of self-worth know that life is not about what happens to them, but about their response. They don't live in victim-hood and they don't spend too much time feeling sorry for themselves when things hit the fan.

6. "I do what I love and I love what I do."

When you have strong self-worth, you learn to prioritize your own needs. This doesn't make you selfish, it just means you have learned to love others *as you love yourself.*

7. "I see myself in others."

Self-worth requires the belief that the world is like a mirror. If people are judging you, it's because you are reflecting a part of them they have yet to accept. People of self-worth learn to celebrate the difficult people in their lives.

8. "I believe in something greater than myself."

A person with a high sense of self-worth is neither full of himself nor thinks the world revolves around him. He celebrates his "higher power," and if he's smart, he finds that power in Christ!

9. "Every day, I find something to be grateful for."

Gratitude is a daily practice for people with high self-worth. These people appreciate the small and big gifts of life, and express appreciation whenever and however they can. It's pretty easy to feel grateful when things are going well. But you can only become grateful in all things when you learn to detach yourself from your achievements and your external circumstances.

10. "I have a story worth telling."

When you embrace a strong sense of self-worth, you recognize that you can help someone else. You have a story worth telling. So ask yourself what you want that story to be. And no, it does not need to be a finished story in order for you to begin to share it.

Conclusion

Anyone can have strong self-worth. By "anyone," we include you! Ralph Waldo Emerson wrote, "What lies behind us and what lies before us are tiny matters compared to what lies within us." That is so true! You are a person of indescribable worth, not only because of who you are, but because of whose you are!

THIS WEEK'S EXERCISE
Talk About Yourself

It is easy for us to find faults with ourselves, especially as addicts. There's this line I love to repeat to addicts all the time: "There is nothing you have ever done that made God love you less, and there is nothing you will ever do that will make him love you more."

Say it with me: "I'm redeemable!" Indeed, there is something about you worth redemption, something that makes you special. Simply said, you have worth.

This is not an excuse for acting out, nor does it exonerate your past. Rather, the purpose of this exercise is to remind you that you are not defined by your addiction. If you are the wife of an addict, you are not defined by your recovery. We all had great worth before we mucked things up. And no matter how "mucked" your life has become, you still have great worth.

So make a list and check it twice. Write down your personal attributes. And when you do this, remember, your list will not match anyone else's who has ever lived. God made you with all that makes you unique and special.

- _____

- _____

- _____

- _____

- _____

- _____

- _____

- _____

WEEK TWENTY-SEVEN

Anger

The Bible warns, "Everyone must be quick to hear, slow to speak, and slow to anger; for the anger of man does not achieve the righteousness of God" (James 1:19).

Most addicts have anger issues. Many of their spouses do, as well. If you are married to a porn addict, you may not have had anger issues before discovery, but you probably do now. The question is how you manage this anger.

Consider the following story, author unknown.

The Story of the Fence

There once was a young boy with a very bad temper. The boy's father wanted to teach him a lesson, so he gave him a bag of nails and told him that every time he lost his temper, he must hammer a nail into their wooden fence.

On the first day of this lesson, the little boy drove 37 nails into the fence. He was really mad!

Over the course of the next few weeks, the little boy began to control his anger, so the number of nails that were hammered into the fence dramatically decreased.

It wasn't long before the boy discovered that it was easier to hold his temper than to drive those nails into the fence. Then, the day came when the little boy didn't lose his temper even once, and he became so proud of himself, he couldn't wait to tell his father.

Pleased, his father suggested that he now pull out one nail for each day that he could hold his temper. Several weeks went by and the day finally came when the young boy was able to tell his father that all the nails were now gone.

Very gently, the father took his son by the hand and led him to the fence.

"You have done very well, my son," he smiled, "but look at the holes in the fence. The fence will never be the same."

The little boy listened carefully as his father continued to speak.

"When you say things in anger, they leave permanent scars just like these. And no matter how many times you say you're sorry, the wounds will still be there."

Anger Management
Matthew 5:21-25

Consider Jesus' words on anger.

"You have heard it said by them of old, 'You shall not kill; and whoever kills shall be in danger of judgement.'

"But I say to you, that whoever is angry with his brother without a cause shall be in danger of the judgment. And whoever shall say to his brother, 'Raca,' shall be in danger of the council. But whoever says, 'You fool,' shall be in danger of hell.

"Therefore, if you bring your gift to the altar, and hold something against your brother, leave your gift at the altar and go your way and first be reconciled to your brother. Then come and offer your gift.

"Agree with your adversary quickly, while there is time."

What Was Jesus Saying?

We see several points in this passage, that must not be missed.

1. There are two kinds of anger; one is worse than the other.

The Greek language offered two distinct words for anger: "thumos," which was like a flame that erupted from dried straw, but quickly burned out; and "orge," which described an anger that simmered. This is the kind of anger Jesus spoke of in this passage. He is not condemning the anger that erupts, only to dissipate within minutes. Of greater concern to our Lord was the kind of anger a man (or woman) holds onto over an extended period of time.

2. Anger leads to unfortunate words.

Jesus condemns a believer calling another person "raca" (word that expresses contempt) or "fool" (from Greek word "moros," meaning "moron"). Don't get hung up on the specific examples Jesus offers — although the term "moron" certainly fits most sex addicts! Focus instead on the principle that anger leads to harsh words, and these words become the nails in the fence.

3. We are to fix our people issues before coming to God.

Jesus said to the man who came to bring his gift to the church, "Go fix your problems with the person with whom you are angry first." In other words, as long as you harbor anger toward your spouse, your relationship with God will not be right.

The Impact of Anger on Your Marriage

The leaders of marriageministry.org write, "The inappropriate expression of anger on the part of one spouse can hurt both spouses deeply and cause significant harm to their marriage in multiple ways." They cite the following examples:

- Damage to the trust of the relationship
- Damage of self-esteem
- Instigation of fear
- At least one spouse becoming distant
- Sadness, loneliness, and anxiety
- Deep woundedness
- Increased sexual temptations
- Excessive drinking

They conclude, "Inappropriate expressions of anger in marriage can be a major source of marital distress and unhappiness. Recognizing and managing this unruly emotion can greatly enhance the degree of security and happiness you and your spouse achieve in your marriage."

Thus, it is important that you take an honest look at yourself and come to grips with whether anger is an issue in your marriage. By doing so, you can overcome this maritally destructive emotion and discover the joy of peace and harmony that God intends for you to enjoy in your marriage.

Final Suggestions

Marcus Aurelius said, "How much more grievous are the consequences of anger than the causes of it."

Mark Twain wrote, "Anger is an acid that can do more to the vessel in which it is stored than to anything on which it is poured."

If you are harboring anger toward your spouse — justified or not — you are doing yourself more harm than him or her. If you have a lingering anger issue, we suggest couples or individual therapy. But for the day to day issues that bring discord, it is our suggestion that before you react out of anger, you should slow down and think about it. Follow the advice of Thomas Jefferson, when he said, "When angry, count to ten before you speak. When really angry, count to a hundred."

Get to the source of the anger. Search your heart. Be honest with yourself. Ask God to help you see what the source of your anger is. Ask yourself the tough questions and listen for God to speak in the midst of your pain. Finally, choose forgiveness. You really have only two choices: (a) forgiveness, or (b) self-destruction. Choose wisely.

THIS WEEK'S EXERCISE
Anger Iceberg

On April 10, 1912, *Titanic* set across the northern Atlantic Ocean, from Southampton to New York City. Measuring 882 feet in length, with a height of 82 feet, the massive ocean liner was thought to be indestructible.

Then, at 11:40 p.m. on April 14, the unsinkable did the unthinkable. Titanic struck an iceberg that her crew did not see. In less than three hours, the ship had sunk to the ocean's bottom, taking 1,500 passengers with her.

The iceberg is like anger. *It's what you don't see that matters.* It is what lies beneath the surface. You see, anger is seldom a primary emotion. It is usually the façade hiding what is underneath. The Gottman Institute developed the Anger Iceberg as a way to visualize this concept.

Think about something currently causing you to feel anger toward your spouse. (If nothing current comes to mind, think of a recent occurrence.) Now ask yourself these questions:

1. What is underneath the anger? _____
   _____

2. Am I feeling insecure or scared? _____
   _____

3. What is making me feel vulnerable? _____
   _____

4. Am I afraid of losing something? _____
   _____

After taking the time to analyze what is driving your anger, honestly and calmly express to your spouse those underlying thoughts and feelings. Keep the statements "I" focused rather than "you" focused.

Example: "I feel anxious when you aren't home at the time you say you will be. It would help me if you called to let me know you will be late." Avoid things like, "You are so inconsiderate. You never get home when you say you will. Where were you?"

WEEK TWENTY-NINE
The Eyes Have It

B ob has been in recovery for four years. He has a successful track record and his Covenant Eyes reports have consistently been clean — no porn, no dating sites, no problems. Well, unless you count what he does with his eyes when he thinks nobody notices. One person does notice. That would be his wife. And Bob's wife has had it with the glaring at women at the store, the ballpark, and even at family gatherings. "How can he do this if he is really in recovery?" she asks herself.

Jim has been free of porn and masturbation for seven years. He proudly accepts his annual chip at his SAA meetings. A sponsor to three other guys, Jim is disciplined in his routine. He stays off his phone after 10 p.m., he engages in recovery activities with his wife, and he loves to encourage men who are early in their recovery. But Jim has this one little habit. Though a leader in his church, he often gazes at the young women on the church praise team or in the seats around him, thinking no one notices. Jim's wife notices. And she wonders, "How can this godly man be so strong in his recovery when he notices every attractive woman during a church worship service?"

Chip just picked up his two-year chip at his SA meeting. He has provided his wife a full disclosure, no longer carries much cash, and hasn't been to an adult entertainment venue in those two years. He has done serious recovery work. But increasingly, his wife has noticed that Chip stays up late to watch TV. At first, it was all sports. Now, when his wife enters the room, he quickly changes channels. She ponders, "If he is so addicted to TV, can a relapse be far off?"

Bob, Jim, and Chip have a combined 13 years of successful recovery. But like so many men, they still battle with their eyes. The quick glance, lingering look, and occasional stare — they are all there. And their wives notice. More importantly, through the window of their eyes, these well-intentioned men are receiving daily images that their minds will store for years. They are wandering down a predictable path: (a) see it, (b) remember it, (c) act on it.

What's the answer?

Approach #1 — Stop It!

"But I say to you that everyone who looks at a woman with lustful intent has already committed adultery with her in his heart" (Matthew 5:28).

In the first chapter of the great sermon, Jesus raises the bar. The focus is on what we see and think, rather than on what we say and do. Jesus understood that what we do with our eyes isn't just a start to a problem; *it is the problem.*

The answer is to simply stop it! Don't look at women this way. Accept this as sin, inappropriate, and damaging — to yourself and your wife. Don't make excuses for your wandering eyes. Every time you look at a woman, you have made a choice that has alternatives. You don't have to look at women other than your wife, so stop doing it!

Approach #2 — A New Covenant

"I have made a covenant with my eyes not to look lustfully at a young woman" (Job 31:1 New Living Translation).

While both approaches are biblical and wise, let's focus on this one for a bit longer. While our standard must be the command of Jesus, with a clear understanding of the correlation between gawking and adultery, the issue becomes one of preparation. If you wait until the moment hits, you're in trouble. It is far better for you as the addict to prepare for the inevitable moments of temptation before they hit.

Make a covenant with your eyes.

In the days of Job, a covenant was a really big deal. Albert Barnes writes, "A covenant or compact was usually made by slaying an animal in sacrifice, and the compact was ratified over the animal that was slain, by a kind of imprecation that if the compact was violated the same destruction might fall on the violators which fell on the head of the victim."

Note Job's language. He didn't make a covenant with *himself*, but with *his eyes*. He committed to control what he looked at. He was a realist. He knew there would be times when he wouldn't be able to avoid looking at women, but he could control how he looked at women. His covenant was to not look "lustfully" at women.

The lesson is simple. Don't wait until a woman crosses your path to stay strong. Commit, in advance, to your battle plan. Make a covenant with your eyes — today.

THIS WEEK'S EXERCISE
Controlling Your Eyes

You need to make a covenant with your eyes to not sin against God (Job 31:1). If you are married to a sex addict, you have noticed your spouse as he looks at other women. For both spouses, write out the battle plan you think the addict in your relationship should follow. Then share your suggestions with each other.

Battle Plan for the Eyes

_____

_____

_____

_____

_____

_____

_____

_____

_____

_____

WEEK THIRTY

The Power of Words

"Be careful of the words you say,
Keep them short and sweet.
You never know, from day to day,
Which ones you'll have to eat."

We don't know who first penned those words, but the author appears to have been married. The importance of words — especially within marriage — cannot be overstated.

The Bible offers a wide sampling of passages that address the power of the tongue.

"Life and death are in the power of the tongue" (Proverbs 18:1).

"Whoever would love life and see good days must keep their tongue from evil and their lips from deceitful speech" (1 Peter 3:10).

"Let your conversation be always full of grace, seasoned with salt, so that you may know how to answer everyone" (Colossians 4:6).

"Do not let any unwholesome talk come out of your mouths, but only what is helpful for building others up according to their needs, that it may benefit those who listen" (Ephesians 4:29).

"The soothing tongue is a tree of life, but a perverse tongue crushes the spirit" (Proverbs 15:4).

"Set a guard over my mouth, Lord; keep watch over the door of my lips" (Psalm 141:3).

The Six Most Powerful Words

For a couple to heal through the recovery process, they must learn to communicate well. Our ministry offers several resources that help with this, including Recovery Night exercises and the FASTT Check-in. We understand the power of words — to heal or to destroy.

As you seek to improve communication within your marriage, perhaps this will help. Following are some very short statements or questions that will open the door to fruitful communication.

The six most powerful words you can say: "I admit I made a mistake."
The five most powerful words you can say: "You did a good job."
The four most powerful words you can say: "What is your opinion?"
The three most powerful words you can say: "If you please."
The two most powerful words you can say: "Thank you."
The one most powerful word you need to avoid: "I."

The Prescription for Communication
James 3:1-12

If you are at all familiar with the Book of James, you know that this little epistle jumps around throughout. The longest treatment James offers any subject matter is found here, in chapter 3. For twelve verses, James addressed the issues of the tongue. In this passage, we see five things about the tongue.

1. The tongue is a universal danger.

"There are many things in which we all slip up; but if a man never slips up in his speech, he is a perfect man, able to keep the whole body under control" (James 3:2).

James makes it clear that we all "slip up." It is true that we are sinners because we sin. But it is equally true that we sin because we're sinners. James, the brother of our Lord, makes a profound case for the danger of the tongue when he says that if a person can control his or her speech, they can control their whole body.

2. The tongue is small, yet powerful.

"If we put bits into horses' mouths to make them obedient to us, we can control the direction of their whole body as well. Look at ships, too. See how large they are and how they are driven by rough winds, and see how their course is altered by a very small rudder, wherever the pressure of the steersman desires. So, too, the tongue is a little member of the body, but it makes arrogant claims for itself" (James 3:3-5a).

James draws two pictures in order to make his point. First, he addresses the bit in a horse's mouth. He argues that if a man can control the direction of the horse's mouth, he can control the direction of that horse. Then, he raises the analogy of the rudder. Compared to the size of the ship, the rudder is quite small. But even a gentle pressure that alters the setting of the rudder results in the turning of a large ship. Likewise, the smallness of the tongue does not reverse the size of its reach.

3. The tongue is a destructive fire.

"See how great a matter a little fire can set alight. And the tongue is a fire; in the midst of our members the tongue stands for the whole wicked world, for it defiles the whole body and sets on fire the ever-recurring cycle of creation, and is itself set on fire by hell" (James 3:5b-6).

William Barclay writes, "The damage the tongue can cause is like that caused by a forest fire. The picture of the forest fire is common in the Bible. It is the prayer of the Psalmist that God may make the wicked like chaff before the wind; and that his tempest may destroy them as fire consumes the forest and the flame sets the mountains ablaze" (Psalm 83:13-14).

4. The tongue is beyond taming.

"Every kind of beast and bird, and reptile and fish, is and has been tamed for the service of mankind; but no man can tame the tongue. It is a restless evil, full of deadly poison" (James 3:7-8).

The idea of taming a service animal is discussed often in Jewish literature. God told the first couple, "Let them have dominion over the fish of the sea, and over the birds of the air, and over every living thing that moves upon the earth" (Genesis 1:28). Indeed, man has figured out how to tame just about every beast of the wild, yet he struggles to tame his own tongue.

5. The tongue is both a blessing and a curse.

"With it we bless the Lord and Father and with it we curse the men who have been made in the likeness of God. From the same mouth there emerge blessing and cursing. These things should not be so, my brothers. Surely the one stream from the same cleft in the rock does not gush forth fresh and salt water. Surely, brothers, a fig tree cannot produce olives, nor a vine figs, nor can salt water produce fresh water" (James 3:9-12).

Nowhere in Scripture is the contradiction of good and evil more evident. The opposing forces of good and evil meet at the tongue. It seems impossible that a person would spew words that kill, then words that lift in the same moment. But we do it. This is a dilemma we must always keep before us.

Take These Ten Steps

No one ever really masters the art of communication within marriage. We all have something to learn. So don't see this template as the final word on communication. But we do believe that if you take these simple steps, your communication — and recovery — will move forward exponentially.

Step 1 — Get comfortable.

When you have something to discuss, do it in a comfortable environment. Serious conversation needs to be conducted only when both parties are fresh and relaxed.

Step 2 — Give your full attention.

Turn off your devices. Focus on what the other person has to say. Don't plan your next response before your spouse completes his or her thought. Only try to communicate when both of you can give it your full attention.

Step 3 — Make eye contact.

Don't try to stare at your partner, but don't avoid them, either. By maintaining eye contact you are saying that you genuinely care about what they are saying.

Step 4 — Open with "I" statements.

Take the pressure off your partner. Don't begin with anything that is overly direct or confrontational. Own your own feelings and use language that suggests that each of you is responsible for your own thoughts and behaviors.

Step 5 — Invite your partner to respond.

Ask them to share the feelings they have in response to what you have said. Ask for their perceptions. Keep it open-ended and not accusatory.

Step 6 — Don't interrupt.

Stay focused, attentive, and connected. Even if the other person says something that triggers you or evokes a strong emotion, let them finish their thought before you respond.

Step 7 — Reflect back to your partner what you are hearing.

Make sure you are hearing what they intend to say. Say things like, "What I hear you saying is …" This lets your partner know that you really care about the message being conveyed and that you want to hear them correctly.

Step 8 — Use collaborative language.

Remember, although there are two individuals in the room, there is also a relationship. As therapists like to say, "There are three clients in the room — husband, wife, and relationship." Keep your focus on the relationship, not your turf.

Step 9 — Convey solutions with humility.

Say things like, "Perhaps we could try this." Or ask, "What do you think this might mean?"

Step 10 — Keep the communication flowing.

Be willing to listen and make sure you are hearing the message your partner intends to convey. Don't be afraid to say that you need clarification at any time.

THIS WEEK'S EXERCISE
Choose Your Words

Words are a powerful tool. They can build or they can destroy. They can encourage or they can discourage. They can lift or they can depress. Words are a powerful tool. This will be a four-part exercise.

Part A

What are some things you can tell your spouse on a more frequent basis that might build him or her up?

- _____
- _____
- _____
- _____
- _____

Part B

What are some things your spouse does say or can say that would build you up?

- _____
- _____
- _____
- _____
- _____

Part C

What are some unfortunate things your spouse has a history of saying that bring you down?

- _____

- _____

- _____

- _____

- _____

Part D

Share your lists with your spouse.

WEEK THIRTY-ONE

Fighting Fear

"The only thing we have to fear is fear itself." While we might debate the legitimacy of this iconic statement, when Franklin Roosevelt spoke these words, they were delivered with the full force of the presidency as America was plunged into war.

But hear these words from a much higher authority.

"I sought the Lord, and he answered me and delivered me from all my fears" (Psalm 34:4).

"The Lord is my light and my salvation; whom shall I fear? The Lord is the stronghold of my life; of whom shall I be afraid?" (Psalm 27:1).

"God is our refuge and strength, a very present help in trouble. Therefore we will not fear, though the earth gives way, though the mountains be moved into the heart of the sea, though its waters roar and foam, though the mountains tremble at its swelling" (Psalm 46:1-3).

"For I, the Lord your God, hold your right hand; it is I who say to you, 'Fear not, I am the one who helps you'" (Isaiah 41:13).

The Faith of a Nun

A nun who works for a local home health care agency was out making her rounds when she ran out of gas. As luck would have it, there was a gas station just down the street. She walked to the station to borrow a can with enough gas to start her car and drive it back to the station for a fill-up.

The attendant regretfully told the woman that the only gas can he owned had just been loaned out, but if she would care to wait for a few minutes, he was sure the other man would return the can soon.

Since the nun was on the way to see a patient, she decided to not wait, and she walked back to her car. After looking through her car for something to carry back to the station to put the gas in, she spotted a bedpan she had planned to take to a patient. She carried the bedpan back to the gas station, filled it with gas, and carried it back to her car.

As she was pouring gas into her car out of the bedpan, two men walked by. One of them turned to the other and said, "Now that is what I call faith!"

Here's the point. Fear requires a plan. The next time you feel like you've run out of gas and can't go any further with your marriage, take heart. There's still hope. There's always hope.

A Strong Man's Fear
1 Kings 19:1-18

The name "Elijah" was never synonymous with fear. The prophet of God knew no fear.

Call for a drought to punish King Ahab? No problem.

Stare down 450 false prophets? Check.

Call down fire from heaven? Done.

Stand up to one woman? Oops.

We are introduced to Jezebel in 1 Kings 19. After the prophets of Baal had fallen, she sent a threatening message to Elijah. His response? "Elijah was afraid and ran for his life" (19:3).

It gets worse. "He sat under a tree and prayed that he might die" (19:4).

Been there? Wish everything would just end? Unfortunately, most of us probably have been there, and you may be there still. If you have a sex addiction, you just want it to go away. If you are married to a sex addict, you might want him to go away.

God had a response for the man's fear. And the response may surprise you. God told Elijah to do several things if he was to overcome his fear.

1. Eat something (19:5).
2. Drink something (19:6).
3. Get some rest (19:9).
4. Enter God's presence (19:11).

What happened to Elijah has happened to you. Buried in this passage is a little phrase that reads, "The angel of the Lord came back a second time and touched Elijah and said, 'The journey is too much for you'" (19:7).

Perhaps that is you today. Your fear — of failure, the unknown, a relapse — has made this journey "too much for you."

That's okay. There is hope. Always, there is hope.

Fear Factors

There is no limit to the number of things that might cause fear. For our purpose, we will quickly address just three fear factors. Each of these are prevalent in many marriages.

Fear Factor #1: Rejection

One of the basic fears many of us face is that of not having our basic needs met. And one of those needs is connection. We call it "love." In addiction recovery, there is a massive fear of rejection that may wash over both parties. The addict fears that his disclosure will repel his wife. The spouse fears her addicted partner will never be satisfied with just her.

Fear Factor #2: Control

We occasionally refer to someone as a "control freak." Actually, we are all "control freaks." Nobody likes to be controlled by another person. We want to be in control. But when we come to grips with the magnitude of a porn or sex addiction (ours or our mate's), we feel a loss of control. And that is just plain scary.

Fear Factor #3: Past

Everyone has a past. The problem is that we have no promises that the past has passed. The trauma, abuse, and pain — will it ever return? The answer is, we don't know. There are no guarantees. All the recovery work, trauma work, and couples therapy in the world does not add up to a guarantee that there will never be another slip or relapse.

Three Steps to Fighting Fear

Louisa May Alcott said, "I'm not afraid of storms, for I'm learning how to sail my ship." You wouldn't be in this course if you hadn't faced storms in your marriage. The issue is how to sail your ship in light of the stormy gales. We offer three suggestions.

Step 1: Remove the fig leaves.

All of us have fear, but we like to pretend we don't. We have to let our fear out in the open and stop hiding from our mate. Say to your spouse, "I'm afraid of being married to you right now. I'm afraid of being hurt again. I'm not asking you to fix me. I just need you to know me."

Step 2: Own your behavior.

Adam blamed Eve for his sin. Why? That's what people do. If you are the wounded spouse, you have every right (and expectation) to blame your husband or wife for the pain you feel. None of this is fair. When you said, "I do," you were talking to someone you didn't fully know. An affair is not what you signed up for. But what you do next is on you.

If you are the addict, you already understand this. You can't go back and change your past, but you can still change your future. Both husband and wife must own your personal behavior. If you are to ever overcome your past, you must own your part in it.

Step 3: Truly trust God.

Your spouse can no longer complete you, for one simple reason. He/she never could. The first person you should talk to every day is not your partner, but your Savior. Be honest. Tell God what he already knows. Tell him something like this: "God, I'm scared — really scared. This journey is too much for me. I'm scared of where I've been and where I'm going. I'm not asking you to fix me, but to join me on the journey."

THIS WEEK'S EXERCISE
Fear-Less

Addiction brings down an avalanche of fear upon the impacted spouse. This becomes one of life's most difficult battles — overcoming one's fear. For many, fear is so crippling as to paralyze the heart and destroy any hope for the future.

But here's the good news. Because (a) God is not the author of fear, and (b) God is greater than the enemy, then (c) you can overcome your fear.

But it won't be easy.

Let's get started. We will start with God's Word and positive affirmations.

God's Word

Take a few minutes to look up three Bible verses that give hope for overcoming your fear. Write these verses in the space below.

- _____
  _____
  _____

- _____
  _____
  _____

- _____
  _____
  _____

Positive Affirmations

Write out three positive affirmations over your spouse and your marriage.

- _____
  _____
  _____

- _____
  _____
  _____

- _____
  _____
  _____

Your Greatest Fears

List the greatest fears of your life. They may not all be related to your marriage or family.

- _____
- _____
- _____
- _____
- _____
- _____
- _____

Share Your List

Take a few minutes to share the above list with your spouse. Try to hear his or her heart as you hear his or her list as well.

Now for the Cannot

Now take a few minutes and think about some of the ways you realize that your spouse can never complete you. What are the areas of your life that they were not designed to fulfill? After you write these down, share them with your husband or wife.

- _____

- _____

- _____

- _____

- _____

- _____

- _____

WEEK THIRTY-THREE

Date Night

A t the close of a counseling session, the therapist offered the following advice to his client. "What your wife needs is a date night."

"Please explain," responded the client.

The counselor said, "One night each week, your wife needs to get out of the house, away from the kids, and be taken to a nice dinner and movie. It will save your marriage."

With excitement in his voice, the client told his therapist, "Great! You can pick her up every Thursday night while I'm at the bowling alley."

We don't remember everything our pastor told us during pre-marital counseling back in 1983, but we do remember one thing. "Practice a weekly date night," Dr. Sewell told us. And we've tried to adhere to that through the years.

Anthony Robbins said it like this: "Do what you did in the beginning of your relationship, and there won't be an end."

A weekly date night may be the most profound and simplest advice we can give any couple. It is a terrific way for a wounded couple to begin the process of rebuilding trust and normalcy in their relationship.

Why Does Date Night Matter?

Melanie White said, "Dating is where you pretend you're someone you're not in order to impress someone you don't know." Fortunately, in marriage, it doesn't have to be that way. There are several really good reasons to have a regular date night.

1. Date night fuels romance.

Addressing this subject, Jason and Erin Champion write, "Let's face it, the romance was the original draw, right? You both want it and if you've lost it, then you both miss it. Dating will rekindle that spark and remind you why you fell for one another in the beginning."

2. Dating your spouse communicates priority.

This lets them know they matter to you. Merely taking the time to plan a date night says, "You are special to me and you are worth my time and effort." It tells them that they matter as much now as when you were dating before marriage.

3. It's fun.

You should date your mate because it's fun. Exploring new restaurants and interesting sites stimulates intimacy. Engaging in recreational activities can be invigorating. It reduces stress and increases connection.

4. Date night is good for the kids.

Your children are watching you. Nothing tells them you are in a healthy place more than doing healthy things together. Men, show your sons how to date a woman. Women, show your daughters how to date a man.

5. Date night is cheaper than counseling — or a divorce.

It is far more expensive to attend weekly counseling sessions than weekly date nights. And divorce is exponentially more expensive. Sure, it costs a little to have a weekly date night. But the alternative will cost you a whole lot more.

The Biblical Model
Malachi 2:14-15

When you are looking for the prototype of a Christian marriage, the Book of Malachi probably doesn't come to mind. But maybe it should. This is what the final prophet of the Old Testament had to say.

"The Lord was witness between you and the wife of your youth, to whom you have been faithless, though she is your companion and your wife by covenant" (Malachi 2:14-15). There are three words in this passage that really speak to dating your spouse.

1. Faithless

The prophet identifies the faithlessness of the husband. The man who has broken his marriage vows has an extra burden to rebuild the marriage. The greater the infraction, the higher the responsibility. Note, the burden here is on the man. He is the one who needs to step up.

2. Companion

The Hebrew word here is only used twice in the Old Testament. The word "chaver" is most accurately translated associate or colleague. It means to partner with for a specific purpose, as two colleagues would work together on a project at work. Malachi is suggesting that the marriage journey requires the collaboration and cooperation of both spouses. This companionship is fostered by such strategies as a weekly date night.

3. Covenant

The marital relationship is ordained by God. Marriage is the first institution of Scripture, followed only by the Church. And this idea of covenant implies a lifetime commitment made before God. It is God who seals the marriage. This covenant is so strong that God never — in Scripture — recommends divorce. While infidelity provides an "out" clause, divorce is never suggested. Our point is that the marriage relationship is so revered by God that a simple date night is the least we can do to improve or preserve that relationship.

10 Commandments of Date Night

In this week's exercise, we will lay out dozens of date night possibilities. But first, we offer several suggestions on how to make date night work for you. Consider these our ten commandments. They don't quite rise to the level of the other ten commandments you may be familiar with, but we think they work.

1. **Be proactive:** don't wait on your spouse.
2. **Be consistent:** do it every week.
3. **Be creative**: mix things up.
4. **Be frugal**: you don't need to spend a lot of money.
5. **Be on time**: don't be late to date.
6. **Be empathetic:** do what your spouse enjoys.
7. **Be historic:** do things that elicit good memories.
8. **Be energetic**: bring your "A" game.
9. **Be intentional**: make this a priority.
10. **Be yourself:** just have fun.

THIS WEEK'S EXERCISE
Establish a Weekly Date Night

You probably saw this one coming. We put on our collective thinking caps and came up with an exercise we feel is appropriate for the discussion of a weekly date night. Here it is. (Drum roll, please.)

Establish a weekly date night.

Just a Few Suggestions

The number of date night options is only limited by your imagination. But for those who have little or no imagination, we're here to help. Below, you will find a series of date night suggestions. We have tried many of them ourselves. These will work if you work them. But don't be limited to this list. Get creative and come up with your own list of date night activities.

Away from home

- Browse at a bookstore.
- Go out for breakfast.
- Watch a sunrise or sunset.
- Return to your first date.
- Take a dance lesson.
- Attend a sporting event.
- Volunteer somewhere together.
- Go to the beach.
- Find a concert.
- Try a new restaurant.
- Walk a nature trail.
- Feed ducks at a pond.
- Play miniature golf.
- Rent canoes or kayaks.
- Go to a drive-in movie.
- Go for a bike ride.
- See a comedy show.
- Go to the spa.
- Play at the local arcade.
- Go ice skating.
- Visit a tea room.
- Check out a mystery dinner.
- Find a carnival.

Staying at home

- Cook dinner together.
- Eat takeout by candlelight.
- Have a picnic on the floor.
- Stargaze from the backyard.
- Play board games.
- Do a jigsaw puzzle.
- Get dessert to go from your favorite restaurant.
- Rent a movie at home.
- Listen to old records/music.

Getting away

- Go for a hike.
- Visit a state park.
- Drive to see fall leaves.
- Go berry picking.
- Find a new ice cream spot.
- Spend a weekend at a new location.

Next Move Is Yours

List the five date night activities you will focus on first.

- _____

- _____

- _____

- _____

- _____

Write down the dates when you will try to do your next five date nights.

- _____

- _____

- _____

- _____

- _____

WEEK THIRTY-FOUR
Financial Boundaries

A recent survey conducted by Insider.com found that 36.1 percent of divorced couples cited financial matters as the most significant contributor to their divorce. Forbes found that "conflicting money styles" are at the root of most divorces. Compounded with issues of infidelity and dishonesty, financial pressures are clearly at the core of most marital conflict.

For couples in recovery, it is imperative that financial ground rules be adopted. Both partners must be on the same page.

When Dishonesty Reigns
Acts 5:1-11

Let's return to a passage we considered previously. There is just too much in the story of Ananias and Sapphira to let it go with a single discussion. Theirs is a story of financial infidelity. Andy Stanley says, "Greed is not a financial issue. It's a heart issue." Nowhere in Scripture is that more in play than in Acts 5.

Let's review the story. A man named Ananias, with his wife's full consent, sold some property and gave a portion of the proceeds to the church. But they kept some of the money for themselves, which misrepresented their public intentions. Peter called Ananias out, and Ananias dropped dead on the spot. When they found his wife Sapphira, they questioned her about the money. Like her husband before her, she lied and said they had given the full sum to the apostles. And like her husband, she immediately dropped dead.

What they did right

It's easy to sit on the sidelines and criticize Ananias and Sapphira. How could they misrepresent their gift? What were they thinking? But they actually did a couple of things right.

1. **They were in it together**. The story begins, "Now a man named Ananias, *together with his wife Sapphira*, also sold a piece of property" (5:1). Their financial decisions were made as a team. That is important.

2. **They made a generous gift**. With Sapphira's "full knowledge," Ananias kept some of the money he made from the sale of the property, but then he "brought the rest and put it at the apostles' feet" (5:2). While it's true that they misrepresented their gift, at least they gave. That's more than most people do.

What they got wrong

While Ananias and Sapphira are to be congratulated for their generous gift, God makes it clear that it is the condition of the *giver* and not the *gift* that matters most. As with the widow who gave a mite, the measure of the gift was in what was kept more than in what was actually given. (The widow gave all she had.)

1. **They schemed**. We are told that Ananias did what he did "with his wife's full knowledge" (5:2), meaning they had discussed their plan. What followed was a downward spiral that ended in tragedy of historic proportions.
2. **They hid the money**. Ananias "kept back part of the money for himself" (5:2). Would their actions have been considered a sin had they told Peter that they had kept some of the proceeds from the land sale for themselves? We really don't know. But what seems clear is that it was the lie that was condemned.
3. **They lied to man**. Peter pointed out that the couple's lie was first to man (5:4). This alone was worthy of judgment.
4. **They lied to God**. Their most grievous mistake was called out by Peter. "Then Peter said, 'Ananias, how is it that Satan has so filled your heart that you have lied to the Holy Spirit and have kept for yourself some of the money you received for the land? Didn't it belong to you before it was sold? And after it was sold, wasn't the money at your disposal? What made you think of doing such a thing? You have not lied just to human beings, but to God'" (5:3-4).
5. **They were not on the same page**. The end of the story is fascinating. After Ananias was called out, he died (5:6). And after Sapphira lied, she too was called out and died (5:10). But they were not together. In fact, it was a full three hours after Ananias' death that Sapphira came looking for him (5:7). Clearly, they no longer stuck together in this plan. They were no longer together.

Sound Financial Principles

There are numerous principles which are helpful to anyone who seeks financial peace of mind. The following suggestions are both biblical and common sense. For further insight, we suggesting consulting daveramsey.com.

1. Maintain a joint bank account.

Many couples, especially younger ones, think that separate accounts will reduce marital conflict. Each person, they reason, tracks his or her own assets. But this is in total contradiction to "the two become one." Whitney Ditlow, a financial adviser at Northwestern Mutual in Miami, Florida, says, "A joint account builds trust and gives you full disclosure."

2. Keep all purchases out in the open.

Rachel Cruze, a two-time #1 best-selling author, says, "Being unfaithful to your spouse doesn't always involve an affair. Sometimes it's when you're unfaithful to a shared financial goal by opening a side bank account or stashing away cash. That's deceitful. The same applies if you have a credit card your spouse knows nothing about." Still, 33 percent confess to hiding financial assets from their spouse.

3. Appoint a family CFO.

"Having a chief financial officer makes for more efficient operations — it's' not a battle each month to decide who keeps track of spending or who'll do the taxes," writes Molly Stanifer, a certified financial planner at Old Peak Finance in Traverse City, Michigan. This doesn't mean one person in the family has to do everything that is financially related, but it does mean one person bears the brunt of the everyday responsibility.

4. Manage (and eliminate) your debt.

In 86 percent of marriages, at least one person is in debt, according to a survey from SoFi, a personal finance company. Debt, as a financial principle, is always to be avoided. And debt brought into the marriage by either partner must be reduced, then eliminated, as soon as possible. The Bible says, "The foolish man borrows" (Psalm 37:21).

5. Prepare for windfalls.

It is smart to have a plan for financial blessings before they come. Manisha Thakor, vice president of financial well-being at Brighton Jones in Seattle, recommends deciding how you will parcel out the money before you get it. It is recommended that you put 90 percent of any windfall toward savings, investments, and debt.

6. Give.

The Bible says, "Give, and it shall be given to you" (Luke 6:38). The purpose of tithing was to teach the people of Israel to put God first in their lives

(Deuteronomy 14:23). Supporting your church and other Christian causes is a good way to stay on track with your spouse.

7. Save.

Saving is a sound biblical principle. The Scripture teaches, "There is treasure to be desired and oil in the dwelling of the wise; but a foolish man spends it all" (Proverbs 21:20). Here's an example of the power of saving. If a couple would save just $1,000 a year for 14 years, with a wise investment of six percent, they would reap a total of $24,672.56 at the end of those 15 years.

8. Enjoy what you have.

The secret to happiness is not to get what makes you happy, but to be happy with what you already have. "Be content with such things as you have," the Bible says (Hebrews 13:5). As one old-timer said it, "If you aren't happy with what you have, what makes you think that having more of it will make you happier?"

9. Get on a budget.

No one would run his business without keeping good records. It is just as crazy to run a household without a budget. To budget simply means to plan for what you will earn and spend. We can name about a dozen reasons to get on a budget, and can't think of a single reason not to.

10. Work hard.

The Scripture is clear: "In all labor there is profit, but the talk of the lips tends only to poverty" (Proverbs 14:23). "He who tills his land shall have plenty of bread" (Proverbs 28:19). There is no more sound financial principle than that of hard work, nor is there a substitute for getting up early, working hard, and staying consistent.

11. Seek Godly counsel.

"Without counsel purposes are disappointed, but in the multitude of counselors they are established" (Proverbs 15:22). Before buying a car, a house, or borrowing money, seek wise counsel from someone who has the wisdom and experience to guide you to make productive financial decisions.

How to Feel Safe

We have offered several principles that apply to every couple. But what about the couple who has been rocked by sexual addiction and dishonesty? Specifically, what can the addict do to rebuild trust and provide a sense of safety within his spouse?

1. No hidden accounts

This should go without saying. There should be no hidden accounts. The same applies to anything of value. We suggest maintaining a current appraisal and listing of all valuables which might be liquidated for nefarious reasons.

2. Limit of $20

If there is a history of the husband spending cash on his addiction, it is a good idea to limit the amount of cash he carries at any time. Even if he doesn't intend to act out with the cash, this removes temptations. The exception to the $20 rule is for travel. That's where our next tip comes into play.

3. Receipts, receipts, receipts

The husband — assuming he's the addict — must keep all receipts for any purchase. By producing these receipts at the end of each day, he is slowly giving his wife the peace of mind she so desperately needs.

THIS WEEK'S EXERCISE
Put Boundaries in Place

Financial accountability is critical to recovery for couples. Of course, the degree to which you should put boundaries in place will be largely determined by the nature of past indiscretions. For families in which one of the partners has a history of hiding cash or secret/nefarious spending, these guardrails can't be put in place soon enough.

Check the specific financial changes or decisions you will discuss as a couple:

- Joint bank account _____
- Limited cash for one or both spouses _____
- Get on a budget _____
- Tear up a credit card _____
- No hidden cash _____
- Eliminating debt _____
- See financial advisor _____
- Keep all receipts _____
- Change in roles for paying bills, balancing checkbook, etc. _____
- Setting financial goals _____
- Other _____
- Other _____
- Other _____

WEEK THIRTY-FIVE

Keeping Score

Several years ago, I (Mark) read about a Little League game in Ohio. The coaches informed their players that the league had adopted a new rule. They would no longer keep score, as they didn't want either team to go home feeling like losers. Everyone would be considered a winner.

They played the game according to normal rules. When it was over, one team left the field with a spirit of celebration, while the other team was noticeably down. The reason? As it turned out, with no prompting from any of the coaches, the players were keeping score on their own.

That's what people do. We are natural born scorekeepers.

Transfer that into your marriage and you'll have trouble. One counselor said it like this: "Happily married people know that keeping score is what unhappily married people do." Something inside of us tells us that keeping score isn't healthy — even after betrayal. But we do it anyway. Why? Because that's what people do. We are natural born scorekeepers.

The Anatomy of an Apology

If you as the offending spouse want to see your scoreboard removed, start here — with a sincere apology for the damage you have caused. In 12-Step work, this is Step 9. At this point in recovery, the addict makes amends to those he has hurt. Our purpose here is not to replicate that, as it is a somewhat lengthy and detailed process. Let us simply offer a very understandable five-point description of a genuine apology.

A real apology requires five things . . .

1. Freely admitting fault
2. Fully accepting responsibility
3. Humbly asking for forgiveness
4. Immediately changing behavior
5. Actively rebuilding trust

Two Scoreboards

In early recovery, scoreboards are inevitable. While the couple should begin moving away from keeping score as soon as possible, we understand that, as with the Little League teams — scores will be kept, whether they are announced or not. If you are early in your recovery and still keeping score, we suggest that not all scoreboards are created equally. Some are bad; others are more useful.

Bad scoreboards measure . . .

- Games already played (mistakes of the past)
- Fantasy (what's in a person's head)
- Intent (predicting the future)
- Personal interpretations (subjective analysis not necessarily rooted in truth)

Good scoreboards track . . .

- Recovery activities
- Missing cash
- Hiding the phone
- Hidden phone numbers
- Unaccountable time
- Time alone with the other sex

Biblical Model of Looking Forward
Philippians 3:13-14

We glean from Paul's life that score keeping isn't a good idea. He was a man with a meticulous memory. He recanted his multiple credentials as a leader and scholar. He also spoke of his tyrannical persecution of believers, before he had come to faith in Christ. Then, he concluded the following.

"Brothers, I do not consider that I have made it on my own. But one thing I do: forgetting what lies behind (old scoreboard) and straining forward to what lies ahead (new scoreboard), I press on toward the goal for the prize of the upward call of God in Christ Jesus" (Philippians 3:13-14).

For Paul, life was about three things: (a) focus, (b) forgetting, and (c) forgiving. He said, "This one thing I do." That's *focus*. He spoke of not looking back. That's *forgetting*. And he spent the rest of his life bringing men with past failures — such as John Mark — back into his life. That's *forgiveness*.

The example of Paul, when applied to marriage, would suggest that we are wise to unplug the old scoreboard and put our focus on the things we are going to do now, in order to rebuild trust and intimacy. If you are going to keep score, focus on your own side of the scoreboard. Ask yourself what you can do to put up points for your spouse, rather than looking for ways in which they might fall short.

Three Bad Signs

Dr. Jeffrey Bernstein is a noted psychologist with 30 years of experience in family therapy. He has appeared on numerous television shows — including NBC's *Today Show* — where he has offered his expertise on marital conflict. Dr. Bernstein has written extensively on scorekeeping within marriage. His summary is this: "Harshly judging your partner blocks you from seeing the good stuff."

Bernstein cites three signs that scorekeeping is destroying your relationship.

Sign #1 — Overwhelming bad feelings

Scorekeeping keeps your focus on areas where you notice (or predict) your spouse will fall short. (No one keeps score in order to congratulate his or her partner for a job well done.) This fixation on what is wrong with one's spouse only deepens the pain and lengthens the recovery.

Sign #2 — Destructive communication

Destructive communication is relationship quicksand. The further you slide into it, the further you sink. Consistently pointing out your spouse's shortcomings will only make matters worse. Focus on the positive whenever possible. Otherwise, you will reinforce the negative behavior you seek to reverse.

Sign #3 — Huge misunderstandings

Bernstein writes, "The act of keeping score inhibits your ability to empathize with your partner and threatens to foster resentment in your relationship. This leads to misunderstandings because the process of scorekeeping is inherently biased." Miscommunication can be the deathblow to any relationship, and scorekeeping feeds that beast.

A Simple Plan

Let us end where we began: *happily married people know that keeping score is what unhappily married people do.* The fact is, revisiting traumatic experiences will only aggravate the pain. Forgiving a cheater is less about accommodating his unfair dalliance and more about liberating yourself from the pain of being cheated upon.

Lesson #2 — Give yourself time.

Grief doesn't end in six months or one year. You will carry a sense of loss for a very long time, perhaps for the rest of your life. You have to be okay with that. The more you loved your spouse, the greater the pain of betrayal.

Lessons #3 — Move toward acceptance.

William Berry writes, "Grief is one of the most painful negative emotions that everyone will experience. Acceptance is one way to get through the experience in a healthy manner." It is impossible to process a loss that you have not yet accepted.

Lesson #4 — Expect waves, not stages.

You are probably familiar with Kubler-Ross' stages of grief: denial, anger, bargaining, depression, and acceptance. There is actually little empirical support for this. The way we process loss is as individual as the loss itself. It is better to expect waves, not stages. Waves of grief will visit you over time. Initially, these will often be tidal waves, but they will eventually subside.

Lesson #5 — Don't internalize your spouse's behaviors.

Dr. Joe Kort, in his article, "How Couples Can Survive Cheating," writes, "An affair doesn't necessarily mean a relationship has gone bad." He goes on to explain that a partner's betrayal is usually tied to issues that have nothing to do with his spouse. Know that your partner's addiction is on him, not you.

Lesson #6 — Honesty is king.

Marriage and sex therapist Isadora Alman says, "The one who has broken trust must become absolutely trustworthy and transparent from that point on — disclose what happened and why, and then what needs to change." We are huge proponents of disclosure and transparency. It is key to rebuilding trust.

Lesson #7 — You must forgive.

This is never easy for the wounded spouse. But forgiveness is not an option; it's a requirement — if you hope to move beyond your loss. Ysseldyk and Wohl (2017) conducted two extensive studies on the relationship between transgression and forgiveness. They concluded that in order for a couple to move forward, they must embrace what they call "relational commitment," and this begins with forgiveness.

Lesson #8 — Review your pathway.

Infidelity doesn't "just happen." The offending spouse needs to do the hard work of therapy. This will address several important questions. At what juncture could I have turned back? What were the underlying issues that led me into the affair or addiction? How will I address those issues? What boundaries did I not put in place?

Conclusion

"Walk on, walk on
With hope in your heart
And you'll never walk alone."
Rodgers and Hammerstein

Loss is a part of life, especially for couples in recovery. You cannot run from it, ignore it, or sweep it aside. You must embrace it in order to move on. Learn to celebrate loss, as it is out of that loss that you can move into a better future. It is then that the words of Ralph Waldo Emerson will ring true: "When it is darkest, we can see the stars."

If you are ready to "see the stars," you must become proactive. Marcus Aurelius was right: "Loss is nothing else but change, and change is nature's delight." How can there be "delight" on the heels of betrayal? We leave you with the words we've said so often. No matter how great the loss, *There's Still Hope.*

THIS WEEK'S EXERCISE
One Step Back, Two Steps Forward

You must take a step back before you can step forward. You must identify your loss before you can process it. That is the step back. Don't take too long on that one, though. Save most of your energy for the hard work of moving forward.

One Step Backward

You can't confront something you have yet to acknowledge. So take a moment and write out your loss and all that it has cost you.

My central loss:

_____

What this has cost me:

- _____

- _____

- _____

- _____
- _____
- _____
- _____

Two Steps Forward

Now that you have identified your loss, it's time to process it.

Who I need to forgive:

_____
_____
_____
_____
_____

Ways I will process my loss as I seek to move forward:

- _____
- _____
- _____
- _____
- _____
- _____
- _____
- _____
- _____
- _____

WEEK THIRTY-SEVEN
Owning Your Emotions

The road to recovery is fraught with a boatload of emotions — for both partners. Because you were created as an emotional person, you can expect emotions to speak loudly over the initial weeks and months of recovery. This is especially true for the offended spouse. Judith Wright said it well: "Feelings or emotions are the universal language and are to be honored. They are the authentic expression of who you are at your deepest place."

When we work with couples to develop a Recovery Night, we include the sharing of emotions as a major component in that process. Both spouses must learn to share their feelings — both positive and negative — as a part of their regular check-in.

Let's begin this week's lesson with an example of a true basket case. We have before us a man who, for reasons that make little sense to the rational mind, nearly drowned in his emotions.

An All-Time Basket Case
Jonah 2

When God told his prophet to preach the message of judgment and redemption to the people of Nineveh, he promptly went the other way — as far and as fast as he could. As you know, that didn't work out so well for Jonah. The Book of Jonah can easily be understood in four sections:

- Chapter 1 — Jonah running from God
- Chapter 2 — Jonah running to God
- Chapter 3 — Jonah running with God
- Chapter 4 — Jonah running ahead of God

Our interest is in Jonah, chapter two. We read, "From inside the fish Jonah prayed to the Lord his God. He said, 'In my distress I called to the Lord, and he answered me. From deep in the realm of the dead I called for help, and you listened to my cry. You hurled me into the depths, into the very heart of the seas, and the currents swirled about me; all your waves and breakers swept over me'" (Jonah 2:1-3).

Three things seemed to have set Jonah off.

1. Life didn't turn out as Jonah had expected.

Jonah was a preacher. Like any preacher, he had his own ideas of where he would preach and what his congregation might be like. Then God called him to go to Nineveh, the arch enemy. Not only would this be a dangerous mission for a Jewish prophet, Jonah didn't particularly want to see his enemies experience the grace of God. Jonah's story was every man's story. Life doesn't go as planned. And we have yet to meet the couple who said, "When we got married, we were kind of hoping to one day go through the trauma of sexual addiction."

2. God called Jonah to make tough choices.

The Ninevites were the enemy. But Jonah knew it was God's will that he go there. Instead, he did what was comfortable, and boarded the next boat in the opposite direction. Then God did what God does. He made Jonah uncomfortable. God does that when we make bad decisions. And it is that gift of discomfort that eventually drives many of us into recovery.

3. God gave Jonah space to pout.

Eventually, Jonah figured it out. Just one whale into his cruise, Jonah repented and went to Nineveh. To his astonishment, thousands of Ninevites repented and came to God. The next move was Jonah's, and he blew it — again. Frustrated that his enemy had found God's grace, he pouted and wanted to die.

In short, Jonah was a basket case. He exhibited all kinds of emotions in this short book that bears his name. That's how it is for all of us who have endured disappointment and distress. And that's okay.

Why Emotions Are Good

When we were young children, we were told things like, "Don't cry," and "There's nothing to be sad about." Culture has taught us to avoid unpleasant emotions at all costs. Our primary impulse is to escape these feelings through any means available — alcohol, drugs, food, work, and sex.

Of course, none of this helps. By either stuffing our emotions or escaping them, they win. The fact is, we never really avoid our emotions; we just delay them. At some point, we will confront them — knowingly or not. There are at least three reasons to go ahead and process your emotions, to "let them out."

1. Without sadness, there can be no joy.

You cannot selectively numb emotions. When you do things to avoid or numb your feelings, you are also numbing yourself to the pleasures God intends. God has created you to enjoy any number of emotions. Jennifer Rollin writes, "Think of your feelings as waves in the ocean. They come and go, rise and fall. No feeling lasts forever; anger and sadness are necessary, helpful parts of the human experience. Additionally, all of our emotions contain gifts and help us grow as people."

2. When we fight off our emotions, that only leads to more emotions.

A Band-Aid never healed anything. It only masks the injury. When you have a cut, a Band-Aid is a good thing. But it's a lousy way to deal with emotional pain. Negative coping strategies that numb emotions cause us to feel even worse, long term. But when we observe our emotions, rather than suppress them, they become our best teachers. C.S. Lewis called pain "God's unwanted gift." Accept the gift of your emotional injury as an opportunity to discover something new about God — and yourself.

3. Processing your emotions leads to a fuller life.

Rollin writes, "Anyone in the throes of an eating disorder, addiction, workaholism, or sex addiction can tell you that constantly trying to run from your emotions is exhausting." Indeed, when you are focused on numbing your feelings rather than processing them, you are preventing yourself from hearing God's voice. It is when you become vulnerable that you heal. And it is when you open yourself to painful emotions that you are able to receive God's best.

How to Stay Sane Without Going Crazy

You need to learn to control your emotions so your emotions don't control you. By "control," we don't mean "stuff." But the tail must never wag the dog. For example, have you ever said something out of anger, only to regret it later? Your mood dictates how you interact with other people, how you spend your money, and how you spend your time. It also determines how you react to the challenges of life. If you're a sex addict, one of life's greatest challenges is overcoming that addiction. If you are married to a sex addict, your challenge is to process your pain without adding a homicide to your record.

Unaddressed emotional wounds will get worse over time. And there's a good chance that suppressing your feelings will cause you to learn unhealthy coping skills. Many of us jump from one addiction to another, rather than processing what got us there in the first place. These are your marching orders: acknowledge your feelings, while also recognizing that your emotions don't have to control you.

There are several ways to do this.

1. Name your emotions.

Why is this important? Roger Ebert said, "Your intellect may be confused, but your emotions will never lie to you." You must identify that which you intend to process. Label the emotion. Are you sad? Nervous? Angry? Disappointed? You need to be able to recognize the specific emotion you want to regulate.

Keep in mind that you might feel multiple emotions at the same time, such as anxiety, impatience, and frustration. Labeling how you feel can take a lot of the sting out of these emotions. This can also help you take careful note of how these feelings are likely to affect your decisions.

2. Reframe your thoughts.

Your emotions affect the way you perceive events. For example, if you're feeling anxious, and you get an email from your boss, you might assume she wants to fire you. But if you are in a happier mood and receive that same email, you might expect a raise.

Emotions are the filters by which we see others. The fact is, we don't see others as they are; we see them as *we are*. Your assessment of another person's integrity or intent is usually tied more closely to what you are feeling at the moment than to what the other person actually said or did. Whether you are expecting a good day or a bad day, you will probably be right. It is your expectations — often formed by your emotions — that will largely dictate the decisions that will frame your destiny.

3. Do something to boost your mood.

Gretchen Rubin said, "Negative emotions like loneliness, envy, and guilt have an important role to play in a happy life; they're big, flashing signs that something needs to change."

One thing that needs to change is an injection of a mood builder. Amy Morin, psychotherapist and author of 13 *Things Mentally Strong People Don't Do*, writes, "When you're in a bad mood, you're likely to engage in activities that keep you in that state of mind. Isolating yourself, mindlessly scrolling through your phone, or complaining to people around you are just a few of the typical 'go-to bad mood behaviors' you might indulge in. But those things will keep you stuck."

Focus on things that make you happy. As you engage in these activities and learn to regulate your negative emotions, you will become stronger mentally and more capable of processing the pain of betrayal and addiction. You will be in a better place to handle discomfort and make wise decisions.

THIS WEEK'S EXERCISE
Moving Forward

Emotions are a part of life. In recovery, they are unpredictable and often run in extremes. But our emotions can be some of our best teachers. The key is to process them, rather than run from them or numb them. That great philosopher Ringo Starr said, "That's all drugs and alcohol do, they cut off your emotions in the end." While we do not have the credentials to lead you into a deep process of psychoanalysis, we can offer a few simple exercises that might help you to process the emotions that addiction and recovery have raised.

Label Your Emotions

The first step in processing your emotions is to identify them. For our purposes, we are concerned with those emotions brought on by your addiction, recovery, or spouse. Take a moment to write down the most prevalent and controlling emotions you are feeling at this time.

1. _____
2. _____
3. _____
4. _____
5. _____
6. _____
7. _____

What Have They Taught You?

Don't let your emotions go to waste. Learn from them. Remember, this is not an exercise about actual events or people. Our focus is on emotions, moods, and feelings. So take a few moments and think about the lessons your emotions have taught you — especially about yourself. Give your responses below by answering these questions.

1. What have your feelings taught you about yourself? _____

_____

_____

_____

2. How have your emotions dictated your behavior? _____

_____

_____

3. Which emotions do you tend to stuff or ignore? Why? _____

_____

_____

_____

What Will You Do Next?

What matters most in life is not what happens to you, but what happens in you, and how you respond. Having processed your emotions, you need to respond to them. Don't let your emotions be wasted. Learn from them and let them inform a better future. In what ways will you move forward in light of your emotions?

1. _____

2. _____

3. _____

4. _____

5. _____

Mood Boosters

You need to be good to yourself. This is true, whether you are the offender or the offended. While it is critical to process painful emotions, it is also important to find ways to boost your mood and to lift your own spirits. Which of these will you do this week?

_____ Go for a walk.
_____ Go to the beach.
_____ Listen to some good music.
_____ Call an old friend.
_____ Meditate for a few minutes.
_____ Exercise.
_____ Get a pedicure or manicure.
_____ Visit someone who needs you.
_____ Cook a great meal.
_____ Find a new restaurant.

_____ Other: _____
_____ Other: _____
_____ Other: _____

WEEK THIRTY-EIGHT
Power Struggles

Unequal marriages are not satisfying to either partner.

There. We've said it. A healthy marriage is one that celebrates balance and equality. Yet, power and control are issues in all relationships. That's because we are all "control freaks." If you doubt that, visit a public parking lot and see how many drivers leave the best spots for someone else. Count the number of seconds it takes for your children to fight over the remote when they decide to watch television at the same time. Fly Southwest Airlines and count the number of passengers with a "B" boarding pass who try to sneak in with the "A" crowd. See how long it takes a preschooler to learn the word, "mine."

We all want to be in control. And that can make marriage both challenging and interesting. Now, inject a sexual addiction into the mix and see what happens. In recovery, you have one partner who is learning to let go of the control that governed his addictive behaviors for years. And you have another partner who, upon discovery of her husband's addiction, feels she has zero control.

What could possibly go wrong?

Everything.

Power struggles create choppy waters. But you can learn to manage this enormous challenge. On the other side is a relationship that can be far better than what you have ever known before. Let's get started.

Biblical Balance
Colossians 3:18-19

"Wives, submit to your husbands, as is fitting in the Lord. Husbands, love your wives, and do not be harsh with them" (Colossians 3:18-19).

This passage introduces the Christian ethic of the New Testament marriage. It is one of reciprocal obligation. William Barclay writes, "It is never an ethic on which all duties are on one side."

Before you as the wife turn this workbook into kindling for your fireplace, let us explain the issue of wives submitting to their husbands. Under ancient Jewish law, a woman was a possession. She was owned by her husband, just as he owned sheep or a house. The husband could divorce his wife for any reason, but the wife could only divorce her husband if he got leprosy or became an apostate. In Greek society the woman lived a life of seclusion. She never appeared in public without her husband. In both Jewish and Greek culture, all privileges belonged to the husband, all duties to the wife.

Enter a new way.

The fundamental effect of this Christian teaching is that marriage becomes a partnership. While the roles of the husband and wife are given different descriptors, it is the partnership that is key. The wife is told to "submit" to a husband who is told to "love" her as Christ loved the church and gave himself for it. This is a win-win.

The roles of "submit" and "love" cannot be separated any more than you can buy a pack of gum with just one side of the coin. God's intention for your marriage is that you both have become one. Scorecards are cast aside. Decisions are made in union. And control is shared as equally as possible.

Five Consequences of Power Struggles

It is understandable that both parties want to exert a level of control. That is in our DNA. This is especially true for the betrayed spouse. She (or he) needs to feel safe. And that will lead her to want to know where her husband is spending his time and money. If the husband is to rebuild trust, he will need to relinquish some of his privacy. And he will do so gladly, because his wife's safety matters most. And if he is offended by his wife's demands to see his phone, monitor his computer, and track his whereabouts, he has only himself to blame.

But the goal must always be to move toward joint control. If one of the spouses maintains dominance in the relationship, there are inevitable consequences that must be faced.

1. Apathy

Some partners just give up. They accept that their needs just won't be met. If the wife isn't given equality in the relationship, she may even come to accept her husband's infidelity. At some point, one-sided control will cause the person not in control to emotionally check out.

2. Distrust

If one partner feels that she/he is not being heard, distrust will quickly build. It is not unusual for the betrayed spouse to sneak around in her efforts to feel secure. This means listening in on her husband's private calls, checking his phone when he's in the shower, or monitoring his computer without his knowledge.

3. Domestic violence

With some couples, the battle for control ends with further emotional, and often, physical abuse. Until the cycle of emotional abuse is broken, the abused partner will never feel safe. Her husband's absolute control over the relationship will eventually lead her to a lifetime of horror or a divorce.

4. Erosion

Stephen J. Betchen writes, "Control struggles can last for years; unless they are dealt with, they can wear a relationship down. Couples in this position may experience a constant flow of relational symptoms such as less affection, low sex drive, and more distance." The pattern of control will inevitably erode the marital bond.

5. Aversion

Eventually, one or both partners will develop a distaste for the other. This is observed in couples that spend less and less time together. Many times, a planned separation goes on endlessly, as one or both spouses prefer separation to the pain of control under which they lived for so long.

Signs of Excessive Control

If one party in the marriage is exercising excessive control, that will be pretty obvious. But to be clear, there are several undeniable signs that the demand for power by one spouse or the other has become dangerous to the success of the marriage. Here are just a few of those signs you can look for.

- Chronic criticism
- Cutting oneself off from family or friends
- Veiled threats
- Conditional attraction
- Overactive scorecard
- Using guilt as a tool to manipulate
- Excessive spending
- Spying or snooping
- Overactive jealousy
- Paranoia
- Lack of respect for other partner's needs to be alone
- Presumption of guilt

- Arguing for no reason
- Belittling
- Public criticism
- Sexual demands
- One-sided expectations

How to Bring Power Struggles to an End

Chuck Klosterman said, "Every relationship is fundamentally a power struggle, and the individual in power is whoever likes the other person less." There is no question that unending power struggles damage the marriage irreparably if unchecked. If you want the rest of your marriage to be the best of your marriage, consider the following process in confronting control issues.

All five suggestions are offered by therapist Bob Taibbi, who has 45 years of clinical experience and is the author of 11 books and over 300 articles on marriage.

1. Acknowledge the problem.

Taibbi writes, "An obvious first step: realizing that you're both engaged in a power struggle. Don't worry about convincing the other guy, start by just focusing on you." Before you even think about "fixing" your spouse (a task far above your pay grade anyway), concentrate on your own issues. Remember, we all want control.

2. Drill down.

Try to figure out what is driving your excessive desires for control. There is always something beneath the surface that needs to come out. Confronting control issues without drilling down is like treating the weed problem in your garden by simply tossing more mulch on the weeds. Eventually, they will reappear.

3. Schedule a time to talk.

Don't spring an "I'm angry and hurt" conversation on your spouse when he or she is tired, unprepared, or worse yet, in the middle of watching a good game on television! This conversation is too important to be conducted when one or both parties are tired or stressed.

4. Engage a deep conversation.

Share your feelings, openly and honestly. Do so without making accusations. One thing we've learned is that the issue is never the issue. So don't focus on ancillary things that are more symptom than problem. Tell your spouse why her actions or words are damaging to you, and what you need going forward.

9. What do you think?

We love it when others ask for our opinion on just about anything. In marriage, it is critical to involve each other when processing important decisions. When you ask your spouse for her thoughts, you are affirming her value as an equal partner in the marriage.

10. I need some space.

It is important to maintain boundaries and to practice self-care. Sometimes, this means getting away on your own or with friends. An annual spiritual enrichment retreat is a great idea. Remember that if you aren't good to yourself, you won't be able to be good to your mate.

THIS WEEK'S EXERCISE
FASTT Check-In

It's time to narrow our focus. While encouraging your mate is critical, it is also important for them to know where you are with your sobriety.

Dr. Milton Magness has introduced a format for a couple to utilize in staying current with recovery. This is an exercise that can be done daily or weekly. It will usually take about 15 to 20 minutes to complete this exercise. For further work, you can complete an entire Recovery Night exercise.

Following is the FASTT Check-in which has worked for thousands of couples. Try it this week!

1. Determine a day and time for the check-in. This might become a weekly appointment.

2. Check-in is the responsibility of the sex addict to initiate. But both partners should check in, using the formula below.

3. The purpose of the FASTT Check-in is to keep the partner informed as to recovery activities, normalizing the discussion of recovery topics, and alerting partners to signs of relapse.

4. Follow this format:

- **Feelings** check: What are you feeling at present? If multiple feelings are present, get in touch with each one, naming them out loud to your partner.

- **Activities in recovery**: The heart of this part of the check-in is to share about recovery activities being successfully exercised throughout the week. Share what activities you have been doing with your spouse.
- **Sobriety (or slip) statement**: Share the progress you are making with your sobriety, or the presence of any slips this week. A statement of sobriety might be, "I have remained sexually sober since _____, and have not acted out since that time." If a slip or relapse has occurred, this is the time to share the details with your spouse.
- **Threats**: Share any threats you have had to your sobriety this week.
- **Tools**: Tell your mate the tools you are utilizing to maintain your sobriety. Include all tools you are using from 12-Step work, work with your sponsor, or personal reading.

5. The check-in can also include other items that have been mutually agreed upon, such as accountability for time and money or a safety plan for travel.

6. Listen carefully:

- Listen to each other until they have completed their check-in.
- Don't ask questions.
- When your partner is finished, thank him or her. If there are questions, take 24 hours to process those questions.

WEEK FORTY
Power of Touch

Touch is the first sense we acquire and the secret weapon in many successful relationships. An interesting study was conducted by DePauw University psychologist Matthew Hertenstein. He had volunteers attempt to communicate a list of emotions to a blindfolded stranger solely through touch. Participants communicated eight distinct emotions: anger, fear, disgust, love, gratitude, sympathy, happiness, and sadness. By simply touching the volunteers, the blindfolded person accurately assessed their emotions 78 percent of the time.

San Diego State University professor Peter Anderson wrote, "We begin receiving tactile signals even before birth, as the vibration of our mother's heartbeat is amplified by amniotic fluid."

Fast forward a life a few decades and you often have a married man or woman seeking how to better connect with another man or woman. What doesn't change is the need for human touch.

Jesus understood the value of touch, as seen through the following story.

The Power of Jesus' Touch
John 13:1-10

In Scripture we have about three dozen examples of Jesus healing the sick. On occasion, he did so from a great distance. But it was more common for Jesus to heal people up close. Though he could have spoken healing over the sick, he would touch them. Many times, the sick went to great lengths to touch Jesus, often to the chagrin of those around him.

But it is the touch of the Master with his disciples, as he neared his death, that we want to talk about. It was his example of servanthood, by the washing of his disciples' feet, that captivates our attention.

Specifically, we read, "He poured water into a basin and began to wash his disciples' feet, drying them with the towel that was wrapped around him" (John 13:5).

Of course, if Jesus was concerned that the disciples' feet become clean, there were other, far easier solutions available to him. He could have told them to each wash their own feet. Or he could have washed them miraculously, without ever leaving his chair.

But he didn't. Why?

There must have been something about his physical touch that Jesus knew would bring comfort to his friends. By touching their feet, Jesus was saying three things.

1. "I want to be near you."

Jesus couldn't wash their feet from a distance. To personally wash their feet was to draw close to each of the twelve. And he must have known that by drawing close to them he would bring a connection that could not be realized from across the room.

2. "I'm willing to get my hands dirty. You're worth it."

Personal touch is not without risk. By washing the disciples' feet, Jesus not only got his hands dirty, he risked any kind of disease that might have been carried by the dirt and filth he was wiping away. Likewise, if we are to practice physical touch with our mate, that involves risk — of rejection, pain, and confusion. But it is a risk worth taking.

3. "I love the worst among you."

It would have been one thing for Jesus to wash the feet of Peter, James, and John. But as he made his way down, from one man to the next, he eventually came to Judas, the betrayer. Knowing full well that evil filled this man's heart, and that he was trading Jesus' life for a few coins, Jesus washed his feet anyway. The fact is, sometimes, we are called to touch those who have hurt us the most. And sadly, that may even be your spouse. If you are the wounded spouse, the ultimate example of forgiveness is when you, like Jesus, humble yourself to serve the one who betrayed you.

4. "I'm willing to bow."

To wash the disciples' feet required getting down into the dirt first. Jesus had to kneel. This was an act of humility that required a willingness to get dirty. But it was worth it for the cause of the physical touch.

Why Your Spouse Needs Human Touch

The reasons you should engage your spouse in physical (non-sexual) touch are nearly limitless. The benefits of physical touch run the gamut of emotions. Let's delve into just a few of the reasons your physical touch matters.

1. De-escalation of conflict

Developmental psychologist James W. Prescott has concluded that the origins of violence in society were related to the lack of mother-child bonding. Lifelong emotional disturbances are the result of a lack of touch in childhood. In marriage, a gentle touch reduces tension and enhances productive conflict management.

2. Trust building

Physical touch bonds people together. Daniel Keltner, of the University of California, Berkeley, suggests, "Studies show that a simple touch can trigger the release of oxytocin, aka 'the love hormone.' Our skin contains receptors that directly elicit emotional responses, through stimulation of erogenous zones or nerve endings that respond to pain."

3. Non-sexual emotional intimacy

Interpersonal touch has a powerful impact on our emotions. Studies have shown that a gentle brush of a woman's arm can boost a man's connection. When a couple touches in non-sexual ways, the result is a much stronger connection.

4. Positive thinking

Physical touch brings about an optimistic outlook. Author Sara Menges writes, "This can contribute to an expansion of comfort in social settings." Spousal physical touch generates a positivity that fuels successful approaches to life.

5. Stress reduction

Physical touch increases levels of dopamine, which helps to regulate mood and reduce anxiety. Dopamine is known as a pleasure stimulant, but also serves to curb emotional fear and worry.

Conclusion

Dr. David J. Linden, professor of neuroscience at John Hopkins University, writes, "While it's common for couples to be very physical at the beginning of a relationship, over time, we often get distracted by the demands of work and home and just, well, forget to touch our partners." This is a threat to any marriage, especially one in need of a rebuilt intimacy and trust. Drs. Charles and Elizabeth Schmitz write, "To touch someone you love is to acknowledge their presence and to communicate your desire for them." They conclude that the most important thing any married couple can do each day is to simply touch one another in a non-sexual way.

THIS WEEK'S EXERCISE
Get in Touch

This week's exercise may not be easy. We may be pushing you beyond your comfort level. If you have been married for more than 20 years, it is likely that you have established multiple habits that seem to work for you. One of those might be a physical distancing from your mate. It didn't happen out of malice or intent, but was more a matter of convenience.

Separate recliners and separate bathrooms are a recipe for sanity. But they can also lead to emotional distancing. The answer is to be intentional about physical touch. So we suggest an exercise to be conducted this week. You can do it for one "date night," or try it several times this week.

Set aside time to be together, and practice frequent physical touch. This might include snuggling on the couch during a television show. It could mean holding hands for a walk in the park. It might include brushing her hair, offering a back massage, or frequent hugs. It must be intentional and on a level that is beyond where you generally are now, in terms of physical touch.

Now, record your findings.

Date we focused on physical touch: _____

Activities we engaged: _____

_____

Who initiated the touch:
   a. Husband: _____
   b. Wife: _____
   c. Both: _____

How did the physical touch make you feel? _____

_____
_____
_____
_____

WEEK FORTY-ONE

Re-Write Your Story

T.S. Eliot said, "Every moment is a fresh beginning." For every addicted man or woman, there is a need for a fresh beginning. Fortunately, we have the kind of God whose expertise is fresh beginnings.

The key to writing a new story is to end the old one. You can't walk in recovery while still viewing porn or hanging onto toxic relationships and bad habits. As Seneca said, "Every new beginning comes from some other beginning's end." In order to have a better future you have to quit trying to have a better past. It's time to move on.

There is no better time than now to begin writing a new story. Someone said, "The beginning is always today." Make today your new beginning. You can re-write your story. You can get started today.

Peter — A Man with Two Stories
Luke 22 and Acts 2

If ever there was a guy who needed a re-write, it was the Apostle Peter. Talk about a man bent on messing things up! His motto seems to have been, "Ready, fire, aim." He rarely thought before speaking. While his intentions were good, his follow-through was not. Peter was always stepping in it. There was no less likely candidate among the eleven (twelve minus Judas) to preach the most significant sermon since Jesus' Sermon on the Mount. But there he was anyway — preaching the sermon of Pentecost. So how did Peter rise to the uttermost from the guttermost? Let's visit both scenes.

Scene 1 — The Guttermost

Peter made a mockery of what a Christ-follower was to look like on more than one occasion. But none stands out like the betrayal of Christ. The story is found in Luke 22.

As predicted, Peter denied Jesus three times. First, he told a servant girl, "I don't know him" (Luke 22:57). Then he denied Christ before an unidentified man (22:58). Finally, he denied Jesus a third time (22:60).

Then we find the turning point in Peter's life.

"The Lord turned and looked straight at Peter. Then Peter remembered the word the Lord had spoken to him: 'Before the rooster crows today, you will disown me three times.' And he went outside and wept bitterly" (22:61-62).

It's that final word that jumps off the page: "bitterly." Peter *wept bitterly.*

Peter didn't simply acknowledge his mistakes. Nor did he quietly repent. For Peter, the condition of his heart affected him physically. His cry was uncontrollable. If you have lost a close pet, you know what it is to weep bitterly. If you have lost a spouse or parent, you know what this feels like.

But when was the last time your addiction tore you up inside to the point that you wept bitterly? This was the end of Peter's first beginning and the start of his next.

Scene 2 — The Uttermost

Fast forward just a few weeks and we find Peter at the epicenter of early Christianity. Of all the men the Holy Spirit could have used to declare the foundational message of the Christian faith, did he use John, Jesus' closest friend? Did he choose James, who would be the founding pastor of the church of Jerusalem? No and no. God chose Peter, a man whose sin left him feeling low enough to walk under a pregnant ant. He could have played handball against the curb. Peter was feeling low — really low.

Enter grace.

Before a massive crowd, Peter took a stand. The first chapter in his new life begins with these words: "Then Peter stood up with the Eleven, raised his voice and addressed the crowd" (Acts 2:14). What followed was a masterpiece of a sermon, weaving the tenets of Old Testament history with the fresh revelation of the incarnate Christ.

Peter concluded his message with powerful eloquence.

"Peter replied, 'Repent and be baptized, every one of you, in the name of Jesus Christ for the forgiveness of your sins. And you will receive the gift of the Holy Spirit. The promise is for you and your children and for all who are far off — for all whom the Lord our God will call'" (2:38-39).

What was the impact of his words?

"With many other words he warned them; and he pleaded with them . . . Those who accepted his message were baptized, and about three thousand were added to their number that day" (2:40-41).

History tells us that Peter went on to play a foundational role in the early ministry of the Apostle Paul and in the life of the early church. But it only happened because he was willing to re-write his story.

And that only happened because one night, he got so fed up with his old ways that he stepped outside and did this — *he wept bitterly*.

Getting Started

We ran across some work by an organizational psychologist by the name of Dr. Benjamin Hardy. He wrote the book, *Personality Isn't Permanent*, and he has been published widely. He suggests five steps toward re-writing your story. The following is heavily influenced by his work.

Step 1: Think about three to five key experiences that have negatively impacted your life. Write them down.

Step 2: List each of the benefits, opportunities, or learning that has come from these three to five experiences.

Step 3: Think about your current view of the cause of these experiences. Then, rethink that cause. Is it possible that there might be more to what happened than you initially thought? What would it mean if something else caused the event?

Step 4: Think about how these experiences have shaped your view of life and of the world. Then, rethink your view of life and the world, especially in light of your addiction, or that of your spouse.

Step 5: Think about how these experiences have shaped your identity, and about how you view yourself. Does your addiction define you? Does your mate's addiction define you? Now, rethink your identity. Focus on the gains, not the gaps. How have you grown because of these experiences? What strengths have emerged because of them? Given the difficulty of your past, what does this say about you as a person? What does this say about what you could do in the future?

Step 6: After reading the conclusion to this lesson, move on to this week's exercise.

Conclusion

As with Peter, your past does not define you. It's what you do next that will define you. But you must become completely dissatisfied with where you are before you will be willing to change. The problem with most of us is that we would rather have the life we do not like than any kind of change.

John Pierpont Morgan was right: "The first step toward getting somewhere is to decide you're not going to stay where you are." If you have made that decision, a new story stands ready to be written.

I love the way George Eliot said it. "It's never too late to be what you might have been." If you — and your marriage — are ready for a rewrite, there are volumes that lay just ahead. Get out your pen. Let's get after it.

THIS WEEK'S EXERCISE
Start Writing

For the Addict

Answer the following questions:

1. What is your plan to stay sober? _____
    _____
    _____
    _____

2. What will your marriage look like in five years, should you still be walking consistently in recovery? _____
    _____
    _____
    _____

3. List up to five goals for your family over the next five to ten years.
    a. _____
    b. _____
    c. _____
    d. _____
    e. _____

For the Spouse

Answer the following questions:

In what ways can you partner with your spouse to build/rebuild your marriage? _____
_____
_____
_____

What will your marriage look like in five years if you both continue to walk a life of recovery? _____
_____
_____
_____

List up to five goals for your family over the next five to ten years.

    a. _____

    b. _____

    c. _____

    d. _____

    e. _____

WEEK FORTY-TWO
Asking for What You Need

A demanding woman approached the counter at the produce section at her local grocery store. When asked what she needed, the woman told the young employee, "I want a half a head of lettuce."

The employee tried to explain, "We don't sell lettuce by the half head. You must buy an entire head of lettuce or nothing at all."

The woman persisted, so the young man agreed to go to the back and talk to his manager. When he found his boss, the employee said, "You won't believe this crackpot who came to the counter, demanding a half a head of lettuce!"

Sensing someone was looking over his shoulder, the man turned around, only to discover that the woman had followed him to the back, and had surely heard what he had just said.

Thinking on his feet, the man told his manager, "Yep, a crazy person asked for half a head of lettuce. But then this sweet angel came along and offered to buy the other half!"

In produce sections and marriage, one thing is for sure. You need to learn to ask for what you need.

Maria Shriver called speaking up "the architect for change." That is especially true in marriage. If you want to effect change in your marriage, particularly in the face of addiction, your voice must be heard.

Moses and Pharaoh
Exodus 8

After Moses had begged off from being God's mouthpiece, he changed his tune. With godly boldness he became willing to speak truth to power. It was God's truth and man's power. But not just any man. We're talking about Pharaoh, king of Egypt.

Faced with generational torment and captivity, the easy thing to do would have been for Moses to play along to get along. He could have easily praised Pharaoh, seeking to land in his good graces. The result, it would seem, would be to reap a softer, gentler treatment from the Egyptians against God's children.

But God had a different plan.

"Then the Lord said to Moses, 'Go to Pharaoh and say to him, this is what the Lord says: Let my people go, so that they may worship me'" (Exodus 8:1).

The message only became harsher, as God told Moses to issue threats of frogs (8:2), gnats (8:16), and flies (8:21).

The lesson is simple. Sometimes, with the king of Egypt — or your marriage — you need to speak up and clearly state what you need from the other person. And as with Moses and Pharaoh, you will not always be well-received. But you must speak up anyway.

Learn This Trick

Dr. Steven Stosny writes, "The most important thing you can say to your partner is not, 'Meet my needs.'"

While it is important to speak up, you would be wise to learn this trick first. Ready?

You go first. Meet your spouse's needs first. And ask him what you can do before telling him what he can do.

Before you ask him or her to meet your needs, Stosny suggests that you tell your spouse the following. "I will unconditionally . . ."

- Make an effort to see you and hear you.
- Make an effort to help you be well.
- Appreciate your contributions to my life.
- Regard your desires and preferences as equal to mine.
- Make behavior requests from my core value, that is, respectfully, without devaluing you.
- Acknowledge your efforts to improve.
- Create reasons to be happy.
- Try to feel closer and more connected.
- Try to feel sexier.

Four Suggestions

There will inevitably be times when you need to approach your spouse with specific needs and requests. Of course, this is complicated by betrayal and addiction. But we think these principles are generally beneficial to the process of communicating your needs to your spouse.

1. Share feelings, not accusations.

This means giving your spouse the benefit of the doubt. Never lead with accusations. Share how his or her words make you feel. Never assign intent to your partner's words or actions. No one can deny how you feel, so stick with that.

2. Never say never.

It is never a good idea to say never. Examples:

- "You never say you love me."
- "You never put me first."
- "You never treat me like you used to."
- "You never let me choose where we eat."

Another word you need to drop from your vocabular is "always."

- "You always talk like that."
- "You always look at other men/women."
- "You always compare me to others."
- "You always make us late to church."

3. Don't use victimized language.

Dr. Lisa Firestone writes, "Refusing to act victimized is an important principle in general. When you talk about what you want, steer clear of speaking in ways that sound victimized or childish. Maintaining a victim role leads to chronic passivity." Don't play the victim; play the partner.

4. Stay vulnerable.

It is hard for many of us to say what we want out loud. When you do express your needs to your spouse, do it directly, but in a vulnerable way. Don't act entitled. Ask questions; don't make demands. Let your husband or wife know that you cherish them, regardless of how well they meet a specific need or desire.

THIS WEEK'S EXERCISE
Open Up, Speak Up

This week's exercise is simple. (Notice, we didn't say "easy.") We all have unmet needs, and all of us can certainly do a better job of meeting the needs and desires of our spouse. This is a good time to start. So follow the simple three steps below, and all your problems will be solved!

Trauma you are facing now

List examples of tests you are now facing. Of greatest interest for our purposes will be the trauma of your sexual addiction or brought on by the sexual betrayal of your spouse. With each example, also write out the initial steps you will integrate into the healing process.

Example #1: _____
_____
_____
_____
_____

Example #2: _____
_____
_____
_____
_____

WEEK FORTY-FOUR
Guardrails

T hey're everywhere. We mostly think of them being along highways, especially in the mountains. But we also find them on hospital beds, on elevated decks, on piers, and at sports arenas and stadiums. Guardrails.

There's another place we find them — in recovery. Wherever you find successful recovery you will also find secure guardrails.

In the introduction to his message series called "Guardrails," Andy Stanley says, "Guardrails are a system designed to keep something from straying into dangerous or off-limit areas."

When we think of guardrails in terms of recovery, we generally think of guidelines the addict needs to have in place in order to stay sober. But these are important for the spouse, as well. She needs her own guardrails, and he needs guardrails that not only keep him sober, but instill confidence in his wife.

Paul Had Guardrails
Ephesians 5:15-18

"Be very careful, then, how you live — not as unwise but as wise, making the most of every opportunity, because the days are evil. Therefore. do not be foolish, but understand what the Lord's will is. Do not get drunk on wine, which leads to debauchery. Instead, be filled with the Holy Spirit."

There is a lot to unpack here.

"Be careful how you live."

The Greek word translated "live" really means "walk." Paul is assuming movement in each of our lives. We are on a journey, or walk. And as we walk, we are told to "be careful."

Have you ever seen someone walk as they text? They inevitably run into a light pole, a stop sign, or another person. At least that's what I (Mark) have done in the past! The answer, of course, is to "be careful." The same is true with recovery. Guardrails keep our line of sight where it should be.

"Not as unwise but as wise."

Paul's concern here is not knowledge. Paul didn't tell the church of Ephesus to learn something they didn't already know, but to do something they hadn't already done. Wisdom is not knowledge; it is the application of knowledge. Wisdom teaches us something from our past.

"Because the days are evil."

Need we comment on this? There has never been a time when porn and sexual betrayal were more rampant. Indeed, the days are evil. Our response must be to put up every guardrail we can find, in order to stay on the road of recovery. Otherwise, we will be destined to swerve into the ditch.

How Guardrails Work

Wise Solomon wrote, "The prudent sees danger and hides himself, but the simple go on and suffer for it" (Proverbs 22:3).

Guardrails are never placed in the danger zone because they are meant to keep us out of the danger zone. That's how they work. We need to back off before we hit the rails. Wisdom says to stay as far back from the edge as possible.

When I (Mark) was twelve, we went on a family vacation to California. As Dad was driving up the coastal highway, I was scared to death! For a boy from flat Texas, the drop-off — if Dad went over the guardrail — would have been deadly. So what did Dad do? He stayed as far back as possible. The rails served as a firm warning. "Stay back for your own safety!"

In recovery, we are to place multiple guardrails in our lives for the same reason.

Two Kinds of Guardrails

Guardrails are erected from one of two perspectives: external and internal. Externally placed guardrails are put up by others, on our behalf. For example, the wife may ask her husband (assuming he's the offender) to phone home every ten minutes on his way home from work. That would be an external guardrail.

An internal guardrail is put in place by the porn addict, without him being asked to do so. For example, he might decide to never be alone with a woman at work, to never talk about personal issues with women outside his family, or to never google a woman for any reason that is not somehow work-related.

How to Put Up Guardrails

If you are committed to recovery and to your spouse's peace of mind, you might consider the following process to erecting helpful guardrails. This is not about the guardrails themselves, but the thoughtful means by which you put them up.

1. Embrace your guardrails.

If you have a few external guardrails — put up at the request of your spouse — it is still important that you embrace them as if they were your own idea. Remember, your partner needs to feel safe. And you should be willing to do whatever is necessary to achieve that.

2. Be specific.

"I will not be on my computer late at night" is a terrible guardrail. A better option would be, "I will not be on my computer past 10:00 at night." Your guardrails need to be detailed and clear. And we suggest you put them in writing.

3. Write down the reason for your guardrails.

It's true that you may have guardrails that mostly seem unnecessary. It is also true that you can drive for 1,000 miles without ever getting close to a highway guardrail. But it is there when you need it. Write down the reason for the rail — your safety, and your partner's.

4. Review your guardrails regularly.

As you grow in your recovery and confidence, the guardrails may change a bit. The bottom line is that the offending spouse needs to recognize the needs of his or her partner. The offended spouse needs a safety plan, of which the guardrails are a part.

Specific Examples of Good Guardrails

There is no limit to the good guardrails you might need to put in place. Consult your partner when formulating your list. Both spouses should have their own list — for themselves and for each other. Following are just a few examples of guardrails that might work for you.

- No lunches alone with the opposite sex
- No car rides with the opposite sex
- No Googling anyone of the opposite sex
- No Facebook "friends" your spouse is not aware of

- No texting of anyone of the opposite sex without your spouse's knowledge
- No "R" rated movies
- No hidden cash
- No secret bank accounts
- Full access to phone
- Full access to computers
- Full access to personal schedule
- Full knowledge of personal location at all times

THIS WEEK'S EXERCISE
Put Up the Guardrails

Let's get to work. This exercise will focus on both kinds of guardrails — external and internal. This will be very straightforward.

Internal Guardrails — List the guardrails you will put up for yourself.

- _____
- _____
- _____
- _____
- _____
- _____
- _____

External Guardrails — List the guardrails you would like your spouse to put up.

- _____
- _____
- _____
- _____
- _____
- _____
- _____

Share Notes — Discuss these lists with your spouse and write down at least three guardrails you agree to put in place for yourself.

- _____

- _____

- _____

WEEK FORTY-FIVE

Intimate Connection

We have a friend who has always had dogs. For as long as he remembers, he has had a dog as his constant companion. Daily walks, car rides, vacations, sharing the bed at night — his dogs were always with him. He quipped, "I never knew what it was to sleep alone until I got married."

We have been married for 38 years. We have had a dog every one of those years. So we understand the value of pets. We are wired for intimacy. That's why God said it was not good that man should be alone (Genesis 2:18). And that is why he created marriage.

Who should you marry? James Dobson has a great answer: "Don't marry the person you think you can live with; marry the individual you think you can't live without."

When we met in 1979, it didn't take long. We quickly became best friends. And that has carried us all these years. Intimacy includes sex, but it is a lot more than that. Especially for couples whose marriages have been rocked by betrayal, building an intimate connection is mandatory for long-term happiness.

Two Become One
Genesis 2:24

"Therefore, a man shall leave his father and mother and hold fast to his wife, and they shall become one flesh" (Genesis 2:24).

"Therefore, a man shall leave his father and his mother and hold fast to his wife, and the two shall become one flesh. So they are no longer two but one flesh. What therefore God has joined together, let no man separate" (Matthew 19:5-6).

Matthew Poole's Commentary explains this union as "entirely and inseparably united, with intimate and universal communion, as if they were one person, one soul, one body."

Without being told anything, Adam surmised that Eve was "bone of my bones and flesh of my flesh" (Genesis 2:23). Martin Luther translated the word "woman" to be a "female man."

The marriage union was ordained by God. The passage of Genesis was repeated by Jesus thousands of years later, giving further emphasis to the marriage institution. God created marriage as a union of one man to one woman for one lifetime. By leaving their parents to unite with one another, husband and wife are signifying a level of connection and intimacy that is not found in any other relationship.

Ten Quick Connections

While deep, lasting intimacy is the result of years of experiences, hardships, blessings, and intentional work, you can start building a real connection today. It doesn't have to be hard. We offer ten ways in which you can connect with your spouse every day. None of these takes more than one minute to do. So pick two or three and get started!

1. Offer a daily touch.

Don't let the sun go down before you at least touch your spouse. Whether it is a kiss, hug, high-five, holding hands, or back scratch, humans need physical contact. If you find this difficult, start small and build up.

2. Ask questions.

"How was your day?" isn't good enough. Ask direct, pointed questions. "How did that deal at work go today?" "Is there anything I can do to help with that project you've been working on?" "How are you feeling about _____ today?"

3. Express gratitude.

We take our spouse for granted. No more. Tell your mate how much you appreciate their hard work, the job they do as a parent, or something about their personality. Take time to thank them for one very specific thing they do well.

4. Relive a memory.

When two people feel disconnected, it is important for them to remember what brought them together in the first place. Talk about your first date, a fun vacation from years ago, or a favorite park or restaurant you used to visit.

5. Create new memories.

Boredom and predictability can suck the life out of any relationship. Lack of intensity can sometimes be confused as lack of intimacy. Try new adventures. Create new rituals. Do something for date night that you've never done before.

6. Learn to laugh.

Humor reduces tension. According to research by John Gottman, sharing humor with your partner is one of the most effective ways to strengthen your relationship. This has been a strength of our marriage. We love to laugh — often at others!

7. Express kindness.

People in successful relationships treat each other with love and kindness, expressed through kind thoughts, loving words, and kind actions. Try something as simple as posting a sticky note onto your spouse's car dashboard or writing a message via the steam in the bathroom, on the mirror.

8. Flirt.

Dr. Jamie Long writes, "Wear something special like you're going on your first date. Create intrigue. With the words you say and a light physical touch, communicate desire." Unfortunately, too many of us forget how to date our mate.

9. Turn off your phone.

Ignore all electronics — DVR, laptops, Pinterest, Facebook, Twitter, and all i-gadgets. Put them away. Give your spouse 100 percent of your attention.

10. Listen.

You may know your spouse better than anyone, but making assumptions regarding what any other person intends to communicate is a potentially damaging mistake. Instead of assuming what your spouse wants to say, ask questions and listen intently.

Three Principles to Building Intimacy

An intimate connection doesn't just happen, especially for couples who are trying to survive betrayal. If you want to rebuild the connection you once had, you will have to be intentional about it. These principles will help.

Principle #1: Priority

You will have to make your marriage a priority. Take ownership of your connection with your spouse; don't wait on him or her. You need to go first. In her article, "10 Ways to Make Your Marriage a Priority," Sheila Wray Gregoire offers the following advice.

- Teach your kids that your marriage is your number one priority.
- Say no to other stuff.
- Be thankful.
- Assume goodwill.
- Drop the expectations.
- Try a 10-second kiss.
- Go to bed at the same time.
- Learn his or her love language and use it.
- Talk to each other every day.
- Share an interest or hobby.

Principle #2: Process

Joyce Meyer writes, "Becoming one is a process that takes time. Many times, the longest part of the process of becoming one is in the mind. Couples are sometimes slow to agree in the way they think about things." Connection takes time. It is the result of intentionality, every day, every week, every month, and every year for the rest of your lives.

Principle #3: Passion

Get creative. Demonstrate your love for your mate in ways that may surprise. Put real effort into your expressions, on a level that is worthy of the first institution of God's creation — marriage. Here are a few ideas you might want to try.

- Frame your wedding vows.
- Plan a massage night.
- Kiss each other every day.
- Text him at work, telling him how much you look forward to that evening together.
- Make her favorite dinner.
- Create atmosphere — candles, music, etc.
- Write a love note.
- Look through your wedding album together.
- Serve breakfast in bed.
- Plan an adventurous date night.
- Go to bed earlier.

- Play a board game.
- Wash each other's feet.
- Plan an overnight trip together.
- Pray for each other at the end of the day.
- Go for a long walk, holding hands.
- Pick up her favorite dessert on the way home.
- Wash his car for him.

A Final Thought

Surprise is your friend. Research conducted at the University of Virginia and Harvard concluded that people experienced longer bursts of happiness when they were on the receiving end of an unexpected act of kindness and remained uncertain about where and why it had originated. They found that surprise is more satisfying than stability.

Replace predictability with discovery. Look for opportunities of novelty and unpredictable pleasure. In his film, *Annie Hall*, Woody Allen said, "A relationship is like a shark. It has to constantly move forward, or it dies." While Woody Allen may be an unlikely source for marriage advice, this line says it well.

THIS WEEK'S EXERCISE
Pick One

In this week's reading, we have offered numerous ideas which might be helpful to building a deeper connection with your husband or wife. We will repeat many of them below. Pick one which you will utilize this week, or create your own means of connection. Then write about it, expressing how it felt to connect with your husband of wife in this way.

Pick at least one activity this week . . . do it three times.

_____ Daily touch
_____ Ask questions
_____ Express gratitude
_____ Relive a memory
_____ Laugh
_____ Express kindness
_____ Flirt
_____ Turn off the phone
_____ Listen
_____ Go to bed at the same time

_____ 10-second kiss

_____ Practice your spouse's love language

_____ Share a hobby

_____ Do a massage night

_____ Write a love note

_____ Go for a bike ride

_____ Serve breakfast in bed

_____ Play a board game

_____ Wash each other's feet

_____ Pray for each other

_____ Other: _____

How did this make you feel? _____

_____

_____

_____

What will you do going forward, in order to better connect with your spouse?

_____

_____

_____

WEEK FORTY-SIX
Safety Plan

"There was a very cautious man
Who never laughed or played.
He never risked, he never tried,
He never sang or prayed.
And when he one day passed away,
His insurance was denied,
For since he never really lived,
They claimed he never died."
- Anonymous

Risk is a part of life. But in marriage, safety is key. Every husband and wife need to find his or her home to be a sanctuary of solitude, peace, and comfort. Of course, sexual betrayal rocks the offended spouse to her core. For there to be any real hope for a quality marriage going forward, it is imperative that the addict go to whatever measures are necessary to rebuild trust.

When one spouse feels insecure, he becomes fearful, anxious, angry, and withdrawn. A distance between partners ensues. The need to feel safe is primal. Experiencing an emotional and physical connection are components to soothing the pain of detachment.

The bottom line is this — God wants you to feel safe within your marriage.

God's Plan
Psalm 91

It is believed that Moses composed the 91st Psalm while ascending into the cloud hovering over Mt. Sinai, at which time he recited theses words as protection from the angels of destruction. In Jewish thought, Psalm 91 conveys the themes of God's protection and rescue from danger.

This sacred writing has the theme of safety running throughout . . .

"Whoever dwells in the shelter of the Most High will rest in the shadow of the Almighty" (91:1).

"I will say of the Lord, 'He is my refuge and my fortress, my God, in whom I trust'" (91:2).

"He will cover you with his feathers, and under his wings you will find refuge" (91:4).

"You will not fear the terror of night" (91:5).

"No harm will overtake you, no disaster will come near your tent" (91:10).

"He will command the angels to guard you in all your ways" (91:11).

God has set the example for all of us. He wants us to feel safe. And there is no relationship on earth where this is more important than that of marriage. As a couple surviving infidelity, you must take the necessary steps to produce and maintain a safety plan.

The Neuroscience of Feeling Safe

Dr. Dianne Grande has conducted extensive research on the subject of the neuroscience of human connection. She describes the sympathetic nervous system (SNS) with the illustration of a frog.

"When you approach a frog near a pond, he'll leap into the water to get away from you, whether you actually intended to eat him or not. This has been called the 'flight response,' and it is managed by his SNS. If you approach a nervous dog who is unfamiliar with you, he may bite you in order to protect himself from a perceived threat. This 'fight response' is also managed by the SNS. If a threat continues or is unavoidable, the animal may go into a 'freeze' response. That frog who jumped into the pond likely sat perfectly still once he got into the water, hoping that you would not see him."

As humans, we have similar automatic responses to external threats. We may respond in one of three ways: flight, fight, or freeze. We are unable to move forward with our spouse until we no longer see them as a threat. In order to heal, we must first feel safe.

The Foundation of a Safety Plan

A feeling of emotional security doesn't just happen. Certain steps must be taken by both partners in the marriage in order for healing and security to return. The following suggestions will help to build a foundation on which the marriage can be rebuilt over time.

1. Disclosure

The wounded spouse can't heal from what she doesn't know. Almost all wounded spouses want — and need — a full, clinical disclosure. Following the initial discovery of the partner's infidelity, the wounded spouse will go

Christ is free from condemnation before God, so is the sinner who is in Christ. Not only that, but God has "raised us up with Christ and seated us with him in the heavenly realms in Christ Jesus" (Ephesians 2:6). Being in Christ by faith removes God's condemnation and assures us of eternal life in heaven.

Charles Spurgeon described his redemption with great enthusiasm. "I thought I could have leaped from earth to heaven at one spring when I first saw my sins drowned in the Redeemer's blood."

A Theological Perspective

Separating the offense from the offender is, at its root, a theological issue. Is forgiveness really possible? Can the person really change?

John F. Walvoord weighs in with his typical brilliance. "The work of redemption was accomplished by Christ in his death on the cross and has in view the payment of the price demanded by a holy God for the deliverance of the believer from the bondage and burden of sin. In redemption the sinner is set free from his condemnation and slavery to sin."

Let's frame the theological case for redemption around five assertions.

1. God's love is unconditional.

God doesn't say, "I love you if . . ." He doesn't promise to "love you because . . ." That's why it's called grace. Lamentations 3:22 says, "God's compassion never ends. It is only the Lord's mercies that have kept us from complete destruction."

2. Your salvation is not based on your performance.

The Bible promises, "He saved us, not because of the righteous things we have done, but because of his mercy" (Titus 3:5). You can't earn your way into heaven, buy your way in, or work your way in. Your only hope is the grace of God. God's acceptance of you is not dependent on your performance.

3. Jesus has already taken your punishment.

The law of double jeopardy in our criminal justice system says you cannot be tried for the same crime twice. That's true in God's book, too. People are not punished for the same crime or the same sin twice.

4. Jesus understands your weakness.

God is sympathetic and understanding. He knows your frailties, your faults, and how you're wired. And he is patient with you. "This High Priest of ours understands our weaknesses, for he faced all of the same testings we do, yet he did not sin" (Hebrews 4:15).

5. God doesn't hold grudges.

The Bible says, "God will not constantly accuse us, nor remain angry forever. He does not punish us for all our sins; he does not deal harshly with us, as we deserve. The Lord is like a father to his children, tender and compassionate to those who fear him" (Psalm 103:9-10). All of your punishment was paid at the cross.

How Does This Work?

Getting over the theological hurdle is the easy part. Understanding God's grace in your head isn't the same thing as erasing the pain of your heart. The task of separating the offense from the offender is one of monumental proportions. But again, it is necessary in order to find the freedom you really want.

We offer the following ideas that worked for us.

1. Remember who you first fell in love with.

Your spouse's addiction does not define him. He isn't a bad person who occasionally gets things right. He is a good guy with a huge problem that he needs to address. Go back and look at your wedding album. Talk about how you met. Visit some old memories. Make a list of the things you fell in love with in the beginning.

2. Remember you are a sinner, too.

No, this isn't a cop out for the offending spouse. It is just a reminder that every marriage is a union of two imperfect people who are both wired to think of themselves first. If you are the wounded spouse, that is completely on your partner, and he must own it. But remind yourself that we are all fallen people.

3. Remember God isn't through with him yet.

Your spouse isn't what he needs to be, he isn't what he used to be, and he's not what he's going to be. God is still at work in him. The person you see in front of you today is not the same one you will be looking at next year. Give grace a chance, if your spouse is in recovery. Try to focus on the person he is becoming.

4. Remember it gets better.

Time does bring healing. We always suggest that the wounded spouse not make any major decisions for the first few months. There was a time when I (Beth) saw no hope for my husband (Mark). But I trusted the process and am so glad that I did. The rest of your marriage can be the best of your marriage.

5. Remember to take it one day at a time.

Things are rarely really as good as they seem on the best days or as bad as they seem on the worst days. So take it one day at a time. Recovery is a daily process. Give yourself and your marriage time. Healing does not come quickly, but it does come.

THIS WEEK'S EXERCISE
One Step Forward

Exercise #1 — For the Sex/Porn Addict

Make a list of five things you will do to show your spouse that you are committed to your recovery and to creating safety for her going forward.

- _____
- _____
- _____
- _____
- _____

Exercise #2 — For the Wounded Spouse

List the things that first attracted you to your spouse.

- _____
- _____
- _____
- _____
- _____

What is one thing you can try to do to move forward, in the midst of your pain?

- _____
- _____
- _____

WEEK FORTY-EIGHT
Unresolved Grief

Grief is an inevitable part of recovery for every couple. There's a line from *Harry Potter and the Order of the Phoenix* with which you can probably identify. "You care so much you feel as though you will bleed to death with the pain of it."

There is no pain like the pain of betrayal.

Eventually, it is that same love that made you vulnerable to the depths of loss and depression that will help you dig your way out. Leo Tolstoy wrote, "Only people who are capable of loving strongly can also suffer great sorrow, but this same necessity of loving serves to counteract their grief and heals them."

CBS aired a special tribute to Charles Shultz, creator of *Peanuts*, on February 11, 2000 — one day after he died. The title of the show was *Good Grief, Charlie Brown*. That title represented the most famous and repeated line from the entire run of the Peanuts comic strips and television specials.

Is there such a thing as "good grief"? While we are not qualified to answer that question on a psychoanalytical level, we suggest that grief can become good, depending on what you do with it. Unresolved grief, on the other hand, will eat away at you with no end.

We will begin our discussion, as always, with Scripture. Then we offer six thoughts on how to resolve grief.

Comfort from the Psalms

Rather than dissect the following passages, we will let them simply speak for themselves. Perhaps you would benefit from committing one of these verses to memory this week.

Psalm 34:18 "The Lord is close to the brokenhearted and saves those who are crushed in spirit."

Psalm 30:5 "Weeping may remain for a night, but rejoicing comes in the morning."

Psalm 55:22 "Cast your cares on the Lord and he will sustain you; he will never let the righteous fall."

Psalm 119:50 "My comfort in my suffering is this: your promise preserves my life."

Psalm 73:26 "My flesh and my heart may fail, but God is the strength of my heart and my portion forever."

Six Thoughts on Grief

Unprocessed grief will kill you. The trauma of an affair or some other form of sexual betrayal is more than most marriages can endure. For yours to make it, the natural grief that has resulted from betrayal and discovery demands a response. The following truths may help.

1. Grief is not forever.

Time alone does not heal. But time certainly helps. If you are in the early stages of your grief, claim this promise today: "No one is cast off by the Lord forever. Though he brings grief, he will show compassion, so great is his unfailing love. For he does not willingly bring affliction or grief to anyone" (Lamentations 3:31-33).

In *Memories of a Geisha*, Arthur Golden wrote, "Grief is a most peculiar thing; we're so helpless in the face of it. It's like a window that will simply open of its own accord. The room grows cold, and we can do nothing but shiver. But it opens a little less each time, and a little less; and one day we wonder what has become of it."

Early in recovery, it may seem impossible for the wounded spouse to believe that there will ever be a day when she wonders what has become of her grief. But the grief does pass, with a lot of hard work and the passing of time. Grief is not forever.

2. Grief is a test.

Seneca wisely said, "Fire tests gold, suffering tests brave men." Your grief is not a sign of weakness. To the contrary, it is a sign of strength. Only the strongest men and women are able to allow someone (their spouse in this case) into their lives to the degree that they can be severely wounded by that other person.

We all endure grief at times in our lives. The question becomes what we do with that grief. We can pretend it isn't there. Or we might respond in all sorts of inappropriate and harmful ways. The better plan is to wait on the Lord. Process your grief, with the help of a trained therapist and those closest to you. That is how you pass the test.

3. Don't diminish your grief.

There is "Big G" grief and "little g" grief. "Big G" grief results from an affair, catching your spouse using porn, or learning that he has been paying for sex. Most of us understand the horrific pain brought on by any of these discoveries.

But "little g" grief must not be dismissed. Mark Twin wrote, "Nothing that grieves us can be called little; by the eternal laws of proportion a child's loss of a doll and a king's loss of a crown are events of the same size."

If your spouse has only viewed "a little porn," only masturbates infrequently, merely stares at women in public (but doesn't "act" on it), or only occasionally flirts with women at work, he will likely try to gaslight when called out on this behavior. He will tell you that you are the crazy one, that his behaviors are innocent and harmless, and that some other guy at work has done far worse. Stand up for yourself. There is no such thing as insignificant grief.

4. Grief comes in many forms.

This is what makes grief so difficult. It can attack from all sides. Sometimes, grief grips your heart, triggered by a quick memory or innocent word. And sometimes, grief comes under the disguise of something else.

In his work on grief, *A Grief Observed*, C.S. Lewis wrote, "No one ever told me that grief felt so like fear." Your grief may feel like fear, worry, illness, or abandonment. That is okay. Expect the unexpected when it comes to grief. It comes in many forms.

5. Listen to your grief.

Your grief is trying to tell you something. "Slow down." "Be good to yourself." "Wait on God." "Go for a walk." "See a therapist." "Get some exercise."

Grief has many messages, but it is always saying something. William Shakespeare wrote, in Macbeth, "Give sorrow words; the grief that does not speak knits up the over wrought heart and bids it break." Good advice. Listen to your grief. It has something to say.

6. Life goes on.

In blunt terms, Faraaz Kazi said, "No matter how bad your heart is broken, the world doesn't stop for your grief." Do those words sting? Absolutely! But are they true? Unfortunately, yes.

Grief never hits at a good time. The pain of betrayal and broken vows is devastating. You can't pop a pill to make the pain go away. But engaging life is a part of recovery. It's what addiction groups call "facing life on life's terms." You don't get to make up the rules. While it is important to take time to process your grief, seek counseling, and confront the cause of your trauma, it is also necessary to move forward with the tasks of life. Maintaining as normal a schedule and lifestyle as possible will help to facilitate your healing.

THIS WEEK'S EXERCISE
Resolving Your Grief

The following exercise is no substitute for the hard work of therapy. If you have not sought out professional help with a licensed counselor, to help you process your grief, we strongly urge you to do so. Having said that, resolving grief is an ongoing challenge. The following exercise should help.

If you are the one who has acted out sexually, the discovery of your partner has brought you enormous grief. The realization of your addiction has resulted in trauma. If you are the offended spouse, your grief is deep and may feel unrelenting. Write down some of the emotions that have come with your grief.

- _____

- _____

- _____

- _____

- _____

- _____

- _____

You didn't wait until we got to this week's lesson before you began to process your grief. Whether you intended to or not, you have already begun that process. What are some of the things that you have done to process your grief thus far?

- _____

- _____

- _____

- _____

- _____

You probably still feel significant grief, either from your addiction or that of your spouse. What is your plan to deal with it? Check the things you will do to help process your grief.

_____ See a therapist.

_____ Engage a physical activity.

_____ Work on my own recovery.

_____ Pray for God's help.

_____ Read a book that might help.

_____ Attend a retreat or seminar.

_____ Try to forgive my spouse (if harmed by him/her).

_____ Other: _____

_____ Other: _____

_____ Other: _____

WEEK FORTY-NINE

Triggers

O scar Wilde spoke for all of us when he said, "I can resist anything except temptation."

The fact is, we all have certain temptations and triggers that have our names written on them. This is true, not only for the porn addict, but for his or her spouse, as well. To maintain sobriety, you must learn to deal with these triggers. Triggers are those situations which arise — sometimes without notice and due to no fault of your own — with the potential of derailing in a moment what you have spent years to build.

Paul often found himself up against such temptations. That's why he would say, "I do not understand what I do. For what I want to do I do not do, but what I hate I do" (Romans 7:15).

John Piper said it well. "Darkness comes. In the middle of it, the future looks blank. You will argue with yourself that there is no way forward. But with God, nothing is impossible. He has more ropes and ladders and tunnels out of pits than you can conceive. Wait. Pray without ceasing. Hope."

H.A.L.T.

This will probably be familiar to you. In addiction work we learn four triggers to acting out. These are common to most of us, with some triggers holding more power over us than others.

Hungry — We are vulnerable when we fail to maintain a consistent diet. Going long periods without eating makes us restless and irritable. For many, this is especially problematic late at night. It is generally a bad idea to skip dinner, then stay up late.

Angry — Anger is simply an inappropriate way to express pain. The key to overcoming anger is to process your pain. Ask yourself why you really are angry. Many addicts have stuffed their anger for years. Eventually, anger always comes out.

Lonely — The average person of today will meet more people in one year than our grandparents met in their lifetimes. We are never alone, but often lonely. It is critical to build strong community in order to avoid relapse.

Tired — You should strive to get eight hours of sleep every night. Most guys are vulnerable to acting out any time after midnight, if they are still up. It is important to lock down your device and go to bed early. When tired during the day, take a nap if possible.

Bored — Let us add boredom to the list. As with King David and Bathsheba, we tend to get into trouble because we didn't get into anything else. Stay busy. Keep your mind focused. Make a priority of time with God, and stick to a daily agenda that you prepare in advance.

A Word about Fantasy

In the 1980s, there was a mind-numbing show on ABC called *Fantasy Island*. It was about people who went off to an island that represented a utopian existence. Each person was granted their greatest fantasy. Then reality hit and they had to return to their old lives.

One of the biggest mistakes people make early in their recovery is to minimize their thought lives. Addicts try to live their lives on Fantasy Island. It is an escape, a coping mechanism. More than that, it is a trigger that leads to acting out. That's because what we think today is what we do tomorrow and its who we become the day after that.

Since we committed an entire lesson to fantasy in the workbook, we will only touch on the subject here. But we must acknowledge the severity of the problem. One study found that addicts spend 42 times more time on their phone apps and social media than they spend in counseling.

So what's the problem with fantasy?

We find our answer from Israeli psychologist Dr. Gurit E. Birnbaum. In an article published in the *Personality and Social Psychology Bulletin*, Birnbaum shared her work. She conducted a case study of 48 married couples. From that she discovered the basic reason we fantasize: "Sexual fantasy is a way to avoid intimacy."

Paul spoke to this danger with clarity. "Clothe yourself with the presence of the Lord Jesus Christ. And don't let yourself think about ways to indulge evil desires" (Romans 13:14).

In other words, get off Fantasy Island.

A Final Thought

During a battle in the Civil War, one of General Longstreet's officers approached him to say that he couldn't obey Longstreet's order to bring up his men to the line of battle, as the enemy was too strong. Longstreet responded with sarcasm.

He said, "Very well. Never mind. Just let them stay where they are. The enemy will advance, and that will spare you the trouble."

If we are to maintain our sobriety — as addicts or spouses — we must engage the enemy. That means facing down our triggers every day: temptations, fantasy, past failures, complacency, boredom, and H.A.L.T. (hungry, angry, lonely, tired). You must engage the enemy — or the enemy will engage you.

THIS WEEK'S EXERCISE
How to Respond to Triggers

Triggers cannot be eliminated, but they can be managed. For example, we know of a recovering sex addict who quit visiting shopping malls, because in his addiction he had purchased lingerie from a certain store in the mall, then given it to his acting out partners. Any mall became a huge trigger for him.

Again, not all triggers can be removed that cleanly. But there are several ways in which we can manage our triggers. Check the options listed below, which you will adopt as part of your personal plan. Be prepared to discuss them.

_____ **Make a call**. Reach out to someone when you are feeling vulnerable.

_____ **Pop and pray**. When triggered, immediately pause and pray.

_____ **Practice the 20-minute rule**. Stay busy for 20 minutes; the urge will pass.

_____ **Remember the end story**. Remind yourself that acting out never ends well.

_____ **Pray the 3rd Step Prayer**. "God, I offer myself to you, to build with me and do with me as you will. Relieve me of the bondage of self, that I may better do your will. Take away my difficulties, that victory over them will bear witness to those I would help of your power, your love, and your way of life."

_____ **Pray the Serenity Prayer**. "God, grant me the serenity to accept the things I cannot change, the courage to change the things I can, and the wisdom to know the difference."

_____ **Tell my spouse**. Tell him or her what is triggering me.

_____ **Eliminate the trigger**. Get rid of some object that is the trigger.

_____ **Avoid a certain place**. Quit going to a triggering area of town.

_____ **Avoid a certain person**. End all contact with a triggering person.

_____ **Lock down my devices.** Get on Covenant Eyes.

_____ **Become accountable.** Get an accountability partner.

_____ **Wear a rubber band.** Pop yourself when you feel triggered.

_____ **Go to bed.** Quit staying up late.

_____ **Put down your phone.** Don't sleep with your phone within reach.

WEEK FIFTY
Unproductive Thinking

Marcus Aurelius said, "Our life is what our thoughts make it." And perhaps the greatest theologian of our generation, Willie Nelson, said, "Once you replace negative thoughts with positive ones, you'll start having positive results."

We cannot overstate the importance of the way we think — whether good or bad — in the marriage relationship. When the relationship suffers betrayal trauma, one of the residual effects, often for years, is negative or unproductive thinking.

What we think matters. Your thoughts spark an entire process. Stephen Covey writes, in *The 7 Habits of Highly Effective People*, "Sow a thought, reap an action; sow an action, reap a habit; sow a habit, reap a character; sow a character, reap a destiny."

In 1952, Norman Vincent Peale wrote a book that would become one of the best-selling volumes in history. *The Power of Positive Thinking* has sold more than 20 million copies in 42 languages. Central to the book is Peale's simple statement, "Change your thoughts and you change your world."

How to Think
Philippians 4:8-9

What you think is what you become. William Shakespeare said it succinctly: "There is nothing either good or bad but thinking makes it so." Your marriage will only be successful if you think it so. Now is not the time for unproductive thinking.

The Apostle Paul addressed this subject in his love letter to the church of Philippi. He wrote, "Finally, brothers, whatever is true, whatever is honorable, whatever is just, whatever is pure, whatever is lovely, whatever is commendable, if there is any excellence, if there is anything worthy of praise, think about these things" (Philippians 4:8-9).

Let's break that down. Think on these things . . .

- **Whatever is true:** This world is full of deception. And you will suspect much about your spouse, but it may not be true. Learn to get the facts. Don't magnify your worst fears.
- **Whatever is honorable**: The root word here implies honesty. It means to process your thoughts through the prism of truth and integrity.
- **Whatever is just:** The Greek word is *semnos*, which is difficult to translate. The idea is to move through the world as if walking in the temple of God. Focus your mind on the things that are right and moral.
- **Whatever is pure:** These are things which are morally undefiled. For the sex addict, this means to avoid fantasy and euphoric recall. Many of us fall into the trap that says, "It's okay to think it as long as you don't act on it." To the contrary, Jesus defined adultery as lustful thoughts, whether they lead to actions or not.
- **Whatever is lovely:** This can best be translated "winsome." It is the opposite of "critical" or "resentful." We are to think of others in positive terms whenever possible.
- **Whatever is commendable:** One translation has this "gracious." The idea is to view things from a perspective of grace. We are to view things with optimistic eyes.
- **Whatever is excellent:** Think about higher things. We are to raise our thinking above the base topics of today's culture and current events. It is too easy for our thoughts to disintegrate into the hateful expressions that surround us.
- **Whatever is worthy of praise:** We know that nothing other than God is worthy of praise. We are to carve out time each day to meditate on the person of Christ and to focus our thoughts on the things of God.

Negativity Bias

April Eldemire, a psychotherapist who specializes in couples issues, writes, "Negativity often works like a slow poison between married partners." She then describes what she calls "negative bias," which is the tendency for a wounded spouse to think the worst in their partner. In order for the marriage to recover, she argues, both parties must find a way to put negative thinking behind them. Eldemire suggests four ways to do this.

1. Be kind.

Give genuine compliments to one another. Speak kindly about your spouse to others. John Gottman's "magic ratio" can help. Gottman suggests that for every negative comment you make toward your spouse, you must balance that with at least five positive statements.

there were no accusers left, he replied, "Neither do I [accuse you]" (8:11). Empathy does not accuse.

2. Empathy looks past the act.

Jesus did not focus on what the woman had done. His concern was with her heart, not her actions. Jesus was all about forgiveness and grace, not legalism and judgment. Imagine the way this woman must have felt as she walked away that day!

3. Empathy points to the future.

To exercise empathy is to let go of the past and look toward the future. Jesus' final words were, "Go and sin no more" (8:11). He wasn't giving the woman a pass on her sin. To the contrary, he was holding her to a higher standard than anyone. "Sin no more" was his directive. Empathy accepts a person where they are, but is never content to leave them there.

Five Questions

Let's consider empathy as framed by several questions. As we dive into these questions, we will address most of the issues that many of us struggle with in terms of empathy. By answering these five questions, you will be prepared to be a more empathic spouse.

1. Why is empathy important?

Empathy helps us to connect with others. It says you genuinely care. There is no relationship in more dire need for this connection than the marriage relationship. After betrayal, this is especially critical if the offending spouse hopes to rebuild trust.

2. What is the difference between empathy and sympathy?

Empathy, sympathy, and compassion are often used interchangeably, but they are not the same. Sympathy is a feeling of concern for someone else, and a desire that they become happier or better off, while empathy involves sharing the other person's emotions. Compassion is an empathic understanding of a person's feelings, accompanied by altruism, or a desire to act on that person's behalf.

3. Can we increase our empathy?

Researchers believe that people can cultivate and prioritize empathy. People who spend more time with others tend to adopt a more empathic outlook. Several tools, including reading novels and meditation, have been found to help one develop empathy.

4. How does empathy benefit a marriage relationship?

The need for empathy in a committed relationship is heightened during times of crisis or conflict, but there is never a time when empathy is not needed. In one study, displaying empathy for a partner's positive emotions was five times more beneficial for relationship satisfaction than only empathizing with his or her negative emotions.

5. How can you tell if you are an empathic person?

Basically, you are a person of empathy if you are sensitive and overly focused on others. Beware of being targeted by some who will take advantage of your generous spirit. It is important to maintain healthy boundaries and to practice self-care, so that you don't burn out from helping others, even your spouse.

A Final Thought

In a series of experiments, soccer fans were reminded of their love for their team, then passed by a person in distress who wore either a shirt supporting the same soccer team, a shirt supporting a rival team, or a plain shirt. Participants helped those wearing a shirt in support of their favorite team the most, then someone with a plain shirt, and helped those wearing a rival shirt the least.

We are naturally self-centered people. But when we see our partner as "playing on our team," it should become easier to be more empathic toward them. On the heels of betrayal, nothing is more important.

THIS WEEK'S EXERCISE

Let's return to the template provided by Brene Brown. We all have something we need to talk to our spouse about. We suggest you select a topic of conversation which will require empathy, and talk to your husband or wife. Potential topics include:

- A dream
- Personal fears
- Something to improve in your relationship
- Personal aspirations
- Insecurities
- Change

The list is limitless. Think of something you really need to connect with your spouse about, something to share on a deeper level. Then set aside some time to talk to them. And then let them talk to you.

As you listen to your husband or wife, do each of the following, per Brene Brown:

- Listen.
- Hold space.
- Withhold judgment.
- Connect emotionally.
- Communicate "you're not alone."

How did you do — in sharing and in listening with empathy? Once you have both shared, tell each other what the other one did well, and what they could have done better.

WEEK FIFTY-TWO

Helping Other Couples

John Wooden, recognized as the greatest college basketball coach of all time, was a champion for integrity. He wrote what became known as the Wooden Rules. Included is this statement: "Be true to yourself, help others, make each day your masterpiece, make friendship a fine art, drink deeply from good books — especially the Bible, build a shelter against a rainy day, give thanks for your blessings, and pray for guidance every day."

Let's go back to the second "rule" — help others.

When Dr. Bob and Bill W. wrote the template for Alcoholics Anonymous in 1939, they wisely concluded that no recovery is truly complete apart from helping others. It's right there in the 12th and final Step: "Having had a spiritual awakening as the result of these steps, we tried to carry this message to alcoholics, and to practice these principles in all our affairs."

The concept of helping others stretches beyond a person's personal recovery. Over the course of this study, you have undoubtedly learned some things about yourself, your marriage, and your God that are worth sharing with another couple in need.

St. Augustine said, "What does love look like? It has the hands to help others." What Augustine said about love can also be said of recovery. True recovery "has the hands to help others."

I [Mark] remember the day I asked my current sponsor to become my sponsor, back in 2015. When "Bob" said he'd be my sponsor, I told him how grateful I was. He responded, "I'm not just doing it for you. I'm doing it for myself. Nothing helps me more than helping someone else."

Are you, as a couple, ready to help someone else? Are you ready to take your recovery to the next level? Are you ready to be "the hands to help others?"

Let's learn from the Master helper.

A Servant of All
Mark 10:35-45

Two brothers, James and John, were among Jesus' first disciples. They would go on to be two of the four most significant figures in the history of the early church (along with Peter and Paul). But first, they needed a lesson in humility. James and John approached Jesus with a wild request — to sit by his side in heaven. They were seeking recognition of the highest order. Jesus responded with a lesson on humility and servanthood. In his concluding remarks, Jesus said of himself, "The Son of Man did not come to be served, but to serve, and to give his life as a ransom for many" (Mark 10:45).

What do we take from this story?

1. It tells us something about ourselves.

We find ourselves in this story, in the persons of James and John. They were among Jesus' most faithful followers. Surely, none of us would presume to rise above them with our own devotion to the Savior. Still, they were self-serving, and we are no better. James and John were ambitious, and they failed to understand Jesus.

2. It tells us something about Jesus.

William Barclay writes, "With such powers as he had, he could have arranged life entirely to suit himself, but he had spent himself and all his powers in the service of others. He had come, he said, to give his life a ransom for many. This is one of the greatest phrases of the gospel."

3. It tells us something about greatness.

Prior to his assertion that he would give his life as a ransom, Jesus confronted the disciples' wishes with a blunt response. He asked if they were prepared to die with him. And that is his definition of greatness — becoming less. It is when we bow that we rise; when we whisper that we shout; when we serve that we are great.

Bad Motives

Not all service is good. In our research we came across a noted author who has proposed ten reasons we should give ourselves to service for others. We share a few of these motivations to demonstrate that not every book that has been written should be read! We will not identify the source, but suffice it to say not all motives to serve are noble. This author suggests the following motives as reasons we should serve others.

- Quit Pro Quo: in order to get something from the other person
- Good publicity: public recognition
- Resume building: service looks good on a resume or application

We think there are better reasons to help other people! If you are in recovery, you know others who probably need to be in recovery, also. You will want to serve others, simply for their sake. But along the way, this will be a great benefit to you and your marriage, as well.

Wholesome Benefits from Serving Others

The Christian life is all about loving others as we love ourselves. As Albert Schweitzer said it, "The purpose of human life is to serve, and to show compassion and the will to help others." When you as a couple reach out to someone else and help them in their recovery, you will likely notice the following blessings in your own lives.

1. Better health

Dr. Frank Martela shares the results of an interesting study conducted by a research team from the University of British Columbia. The team gave $40 to several older adults who each suffered from high blood pressure. They repeated this for three weeks, so that each person was eventually given $120.

Half of the participants were told to spend the money on themselves; the rest were asked to spend it on someone else. At the end of the three weeks, the researchers measured the blood pressure of each volunteer in the program. What they found was that each of those participants who gave their money to help others saw a reduction in their blood pressure, whereas the ones who kept the money for themselves did not.

The conclusion? Helping others is good for your health.

2. Social regulation

Research has found that by helping others to regulate their emotions, we regulate our own. When we help others, we not only *do* good, we *feel* good. Dr. Marianna Pogosyan writes, "One reason behind the positive feelings associated with helping others is that being pro-social reinforces our sense of relatedness to others, thus helping us meet our most basic psychological needs."

3. New skills

Author Pamela Laughland writes, "Helping others can help you build new skill sets, as you engage them outside your comfort zone." It may not be inside your comfort zone to help another couple with such intimate issues as sexuality or betrayal. And that might be why you need to do it.

4. Newfound gratefulness

Helping others with their struggles can help you see your own challenges with a fresh perspective. You may be taking some things for granted, which others don't enjoy — a good home, sufficient income, and good health, for example. Working with others will help you to celebrate the good things in your own life.

5. Expanded horizons

Most of us have only used a fraction of our capacity in helping others. By getting outside your comfort zone to work with another couple, you will discover attributes God has given you to bless others, which you never knew you had. Psychology has shown that when you focus too myopically on one dimension of life, you will stagnate.

6. Healthier self-esteem

Seeing others grow because of God's work through you will give you a sense of satisfaction and usefulness that can't be found anywhere else. If you commit a period of time to helping another couple, you will receive more than you give. There is nothing that makes us feel better than seeing others step into a healthier life.

THIS WEEK'S EXERCISE
Help Someone Else

Helping others is the icing on the recovery cake. Winston Churchill said, "We make a living by what we get. We make a life by what we give." So let's do something to "make a life." There is a couple out there just waiting for your help, whether in the arena of sexual addiction, some other form of trauma or betrayal, or simply from the pain of life.

Step 1 — Identify the couple

Write down up to three couples you think you might reach out to in the coming days, then come together with your spouse to narrow the list to one.

a. _____

b. _____

c. _____

Step 2 — Identify this couple's primary issue.

Write down up to three issues you and your spouse feel are the primary struggles this other couple has. Then narrow that to one, if possible.

a. _____

b. _____

c. _____

Step 3 — Create a plan to help this other couple.

Aspects of this plan might include dinner with this couple, a weekly meeting, mentoring, taking them through a recovery process, inviting them to your church, or any other number of things. Write down up to five aspects to your plan to help this other couple.

a. _____

b. _____

c. _____

d. _____

e. _____

Step 4 — Get started. Set a date and time when you will start the process.

_____

Printed in the USA
CPSIA information can be obtained
at www.ICGtesting.com
LVHW081221240124
769394LV00008B/158